# CALIFORNIA INTEGRATED

Grade 7

# elevate science

P **Pearson**

Boston, Massachusetts    Chandler, Arizona
Glenview, Illinois    New York, New York

# AUTHORS

## You're an author!

As you write in this science book, your answers and personal discoveries will be recorded for you to keep, making this book unique to you. That is why you are one of the primary authors of this book.

✎ In the space below, print your name, school, town, and state. Then write a short autobiography that includes your interests and accomplishments.

YOUR NAME ........................................................................................

SCHOOL ...............................................................................................

TOWN, STATE ......................................................................................

AUTOBIOGRAPHY ...............................................................................

...........................................................................................................

...........................................................................................................

...........................................................................................................

...........................................................................................................

Your Photo

Pearson Education, Inc. 330 Hudson Street, New York, NY 10013

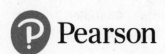

ISBN-13: 978-1-418-31040-0
ISBN-10: 1-418-31040-9
2 19

# Program Authors

**ZIPPORAH MILLER, Ed.D.**
*Coordinator for K-12 Science Programs, Anne Arundel County Public Schools*
Dr. Zipporah Miller currently serves as the Senior Manager for Organizational Learning with the Anne Arundel County Public School System. Prior to that she served as the K-12 Coordinator for science in Anne Arundel County. She conducts national training to science stakeholders on the Next Generation Science Standards. Dr. Miller also served as the Associate Executive Director for Professional Development Programs and conferences at the National Science Teachers Association (NSTA) and served as a reviewer during the development of Next Generation Science Standards. Dr. Miller holds a doctoral degree from the University of Maryland College Park, a master's degree in school administration and supervision from Bowie State University and a bachelor's degree from Chadron State College.

**MICHAEL J. PADILLA, Ph.D.**
*Professor Emeritus, Eugene P. Moore School of Education, Clemson University, Clemson, South Carolina*
Michael J. Padilla taught science in middle and secondary schools, has more than 30 years of experience educating middle-school science teachers, and served as one of the writers of the 1996 U.S. National Science Education Standards. In recent years Mike has focused on teaching science to English Language Learners. His extensive experience as Principal Investigator on numerous National Science Foundation and U.S. Department of Education grants resulted in more than $35 million in funding to improve science education. He served as president of the National Science Teachers Association, the world's largest science teaching organization, in 2005–6.

**MICHAEL E. WYSESSION, Ph.D**
*Professor of Earth and Planetary Sciences, Washington University, St. Louis, Missouri*
Author of more than 100 science and science education publications, Dr. Wysession was awarded the prestigious National Science Foundation Presidential Faculty Fellowship and Packard Foundation Fellowship for his research in geophysics, primarily focused on using seismic tomography to determine the forces driving plate tectonics. Dr. Wysession is also a leader in geoscience literacy and education; he is the chair of the Earth Science Literacy Initiative, the author of several popular video lectures on geology in the *Great Courses* series, and a lead writer of the *Next Generation Science Standards*\*.

## Program Consultants

### Carol Baker
**Science Curriculum**

Dr. Carol K. Baker is superintendent for Lyons Elementary K-8 School District in Lyons, Illinois. Prior to this, she was Director of Curriculum for Science and Music in Oak Lawn, Illinois. Before this she taught Physics and Earth Science for 18 years. In the recent past, Dr. Baker also wrote assessment questions for ACT (EXPLORE and PLAN), was elected president of the Illinois Science Teachers Association from 2011–2013, and served as a member of the Museum of Science and Industry (Chicago) advisory board. She is a writer of the Next Generation Science Standards. Dr. Baker received her B.S. in Physics and a science teaching certification. She completed her master's of Educational Administration (K-12) and earned her doctorate in Educational Leadership.

### Jim Cummins
**ELL**

Dr. Cummins's research focuses on literacy development in multilingual schools and the role technology plays in learning across the curriculum. *Elevate Science* incorporates research-based principles for integrating language with the teaching of academic content based on Dr. Cummins's work.

### Elfrieda Hiebert
**Literacy**

Dr. Hiebert, a former primary-school teacher, is President and CEO of TextProject, a non-profit aimed at providing open-access resources for instruction of beginning and struggling readers, She is also a research associate at the University of California Santa Cruz. Her research addresses how fluency, vocabulary, and knowledge can be fostered through appropriate texts, and her contributions have been recognized through awards such as the Oscar Causey Award for Outstanding Contributions to Reading Research (Literacy Research Association, 2015), Research to Practice award (American Educational Research Association, 2013), and the William S. Gray Citation of Merit Award for Outstanding Contributions to Reading Research (International Reading Association, 2008).

## Content Reviewers

**Alex Blom, Ph.D.**
Associate Professor
Department Of Physical Sciences
Alverno College
Milwaukee, Wisconsin

**Joy Branlund, Ph.D.**
Department of Physical Science
Southwestern Illinois College
Granite City, Illinois

**Judy Calhoun**
Associate Professor
Physical Sciences
Alverno College
Milwaukee, Wisconsin

**Stefan Debbert**
Associate Professor of Chemistry
Lawrence University
Appleton, Wisconsin

**Diane Doser**
Professor
Department of Geological Sciences
University of Texas at El Paso
El Paso, Texas

**Rick Duhrkopf, Ph.D.**
Department of Biology
Baylor University
Waco, Texas

**Jennifer Liang**
University of Minnesota Duluth
Duluth, Minnesota

**Heather Mernitz, Ph.D.**
Associate Professor of Physical Sciences
Alverno College
Milwaukee, Wisconsin

**Joseph McCullough, Ph.D.**
Cabrillo College
Aptos, California

**Katie M. Nemeth, Ph.D.**
Assistant Professor
College of Science and Engineering
University of Minnesota Duluth
Duluth, Minnesota

**Maik Pertermann**
Department of Geology
Western Wyoming Community College
Rock Springs, Wyoming

**Scott Rochette**
Department of the Earth Sciences
The College at Brockport
State University of New York
Brockport, New York

**David Schuster**
Washington University in St Louis
St. Louis, Missouri

**Shannon Stevenson**
Department of Biology
University of Minnesota Duluth
Duluth, Minnesota

**Paul Stoddard, Ph.D.**
Department of Geology and Environmental Geosciences
Northern Illinois University
DeKalb, Illinois

**Nancy Taylor**
American Public University
Charles Town, West Virginia

## Teacher Reviewers

**Rita Armstrong**
Los Cerritos Middle School
Thousand Oaks, California

**Tyler C. Britt, Ed.S.**
Curriculum & Instructional
Practice Coordinator
Raytown Quality Schools
Raytown, Missouri

**Holly Bowser**
Barstow High School
Barstow, California

**David Budai**
Coachella Valley Unified School District
Coachella, California

**A. Colleen Campos**
Grandview High School
Aurora, Colorado

**Jodi DeRoos**
Mojave River Academy
Colton, California

**Colleen Duncan**
Moore Middle School
Redlands, California

**Nicole Hawke**
Westside Elementary
Thermal, California

**Margaret Henry**
Lebanon Junior High School
Lebanon, Ohio

**Ashley Humphrey**
Riverside Preparatory Elementary
Oro Grande, California

**Adrianne Kilzer**
Riverside Preparatory Elementary
Oro Grande, California

**Danielle King**
Barstow Unified School District
Barstow, California

**Kathryn Kooyman**
Riverside Preparatory Elementary
Oro Grande, California

**Esther Leonard M.Ed. and L.M.T.**
Gifted and Talented Implementation Specialist
San Antonio Independent School District
San Antonio, Texas

**Diana M. Maiorca, M.Ed.**
Los Cerritos Middle School
Thousand Oaks, California

**Kevin J. Maser, Ed.D.**
H. Frank Carey Jr/Sr High School
Franklin Square, New York

**Corey Mayle**
Brogden Middle School
Durham, North Carolina

**Keith McCarthy**
George Washington Middle School
Wayne, New Jersey

**Rudolph Patterson**
Cobalt Institute of Math and Science
Victorville, California

**Yolanda O. Peña**
John F. Kennedy Junior High School
West Valley City, Utah

**Stacey Phelps**
Mojave River Academy
Oro Grande, California

**Susan Pierce**
Bryn Mawr Elementary
Redlands Unified School District
Redlands, California

**Cristina Ramos**
Mentone Elementary School
Redlands Unified School District
Mentone, California

**Mary Regis**
Franklin Elementary School
Redlands, California

**Bryna Selig**
Gaithersburg Middle School
Gaithersburg, Maryland

**Pat (Patricia) Shane, Ph.D.**
STEM & ELA Education Consultant
Chapel Hill, North Carolina

**Elena Valencia**
Coral Mountain Academy
Coachella, California

**Janelle Vecchio**
Mission Elementary School
Redlands, California

**Brittney Wells**
Riverside Preparatory Elementary
Oro Grande, California

**Kristina Williams**
Sequoia Middle School
Newbury Park, California

## Safety Reviewers

**Douglas Mandt, M.S.**
Science Education Consultant
Edgewood, Washington

**Juliana Textley, Ph.D.**
Author, NSTA books on school science safety
Adjunct Professor
Lesley University
Cambridge, Massachusetts

# California Spotlight
## Instructional Segment 3

**TOPICS 6–7**

## Gold Mining and California Ecosystems

**TOPIC 6**

# Distribution of Natural Resources

**Investigative Phenomenon** How can you explain the uneven distributions of Earth's natural resources?

🕐 MS-ESS3-1, EP&CIc

## HANDS-ON LABS

ИConnect
ИInvestigate
ИDemonstrate

### California Spotlight 🐻

## Gold Mining and California Ecosystems

### HANDS-ON LABS
**uConnect**
**uInvestigate**
**uDemonstrate**

# Elevate your thinking!

*California Elevate Science* takes science to a whole new level and lets you take ownership of your learning. Explore science in the world around you. Investigate how things work. Think critically and solve problems! *California Elevate Science* helps you think like a scientist, so you're ready for a world of discoveries.

## Exploring California

California spotlights explore California phenomena. Topic Quests help connect lesson concepts together and reflect 3-dimensional learning.

- Science concepts organized around phenomena
- Topics weave together 3-D learning
- Engineering focused on solving problems and improving designs

## Student Discourse

*California Elevate Science* promotes active discussion, higher order thinking and analysis and prepares you for high school through:

- High-level write-in prompts
- Evidence-based arguments
- Practice in speaking and writing

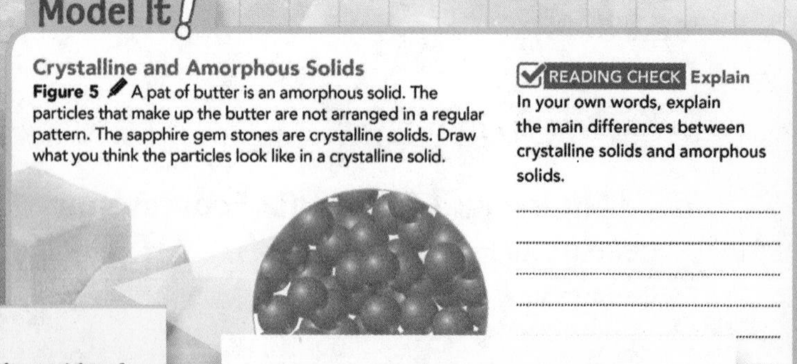

### California Spotlight
**Instructional Segment 2**

Before the Topics
**Identify the Problem**

## California Flood Management

**Phenomenon** In February of 2017, workers at the Orov...

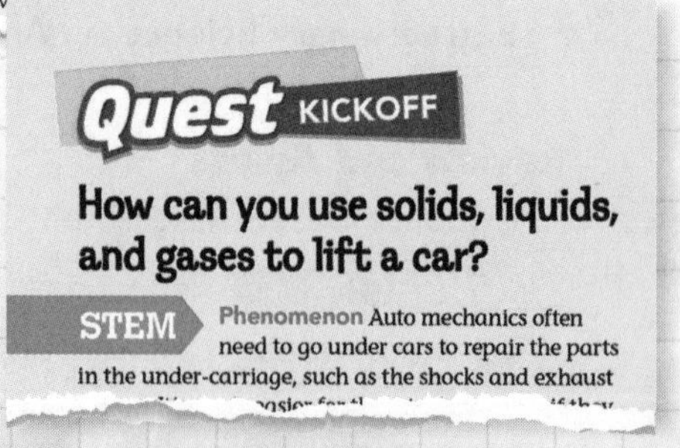

### Quest KICKOFF

**How can you use solids, liquids, and gases to lift a car?**

**STEM** Phenomenon Auto mechanics often need to go under cars to repair the parts in the under-carriage, such as the shocks and exhaust

### Model It

**Crystalline and Amorphous Solids**
**Figure 5** A pat of butter is an amorphous solid. The particles that make up the butter are not arranged in a regular pattern. The sapphire gem stones are crystalline solids. Draw what you think the particles look like in a crystalline solid.

**READING CHECK** Explain In your own words, explain the main differences between crystalline solids and amorphous solids.

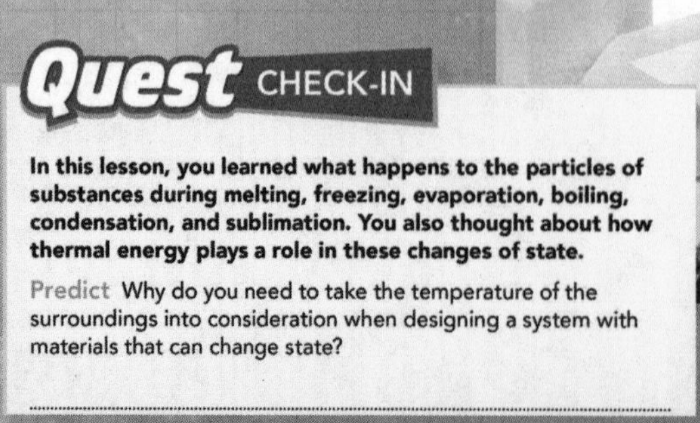

### Quest CHECK-IN

In this lesson, you learned what happens to the particles of substances during melting, freezing, evaporation, boiling, condensation, and sublimation. You also thought about how thermal energy plays a role in these changes of state.

**Predict** Why do you need to take the temperature of the surroundings into consideration when designing a system with materials that can change state?

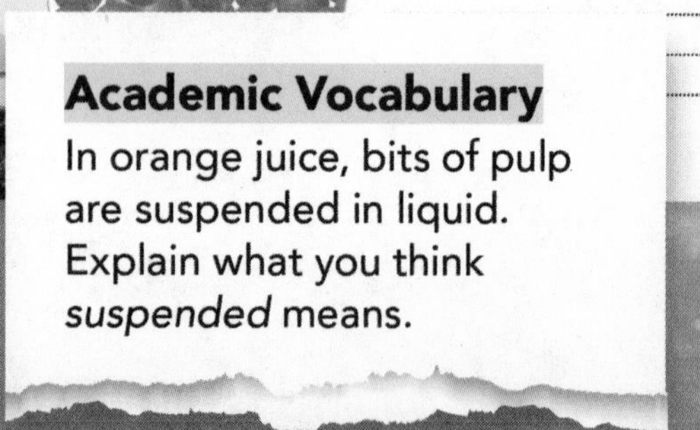

### Academic Vocabulary

In orange juice, bits of pulp are suspended in liquid. Explain what you think *suspended* means.

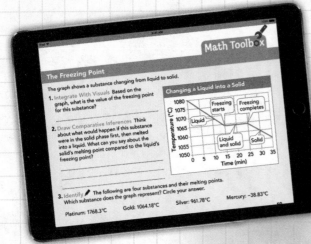

# Build Literacy Skills

By connecting science to other disciplines like:

- Mathematics
- Reading and Writing
- STEM/Engineering

# Focus on Inquiry

Case studies put you in the shoes of a scientist to solve real-world mysteries using real data. You will be able to:

- Analyze data
- Formulate claims
- Build evidence-based arguments

# Enter the Digital Classroom

Virtual labs, 3-D expeditions, and dynamic videos take science beyond the classroom.

- Open-ended virtual labs
- Google Expeditions and field trips
- NBC Learn videos

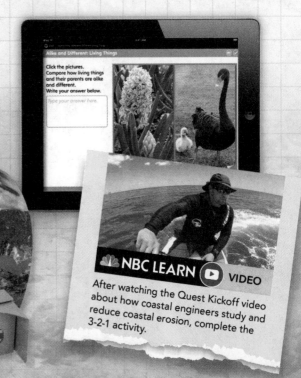

# How does human consumption of natural resources affect ecosystems?

## Explore It

**Look at the picture. What do you observe? What questions do you have about the phenomenon? Write your observations and questions in the space below.**

......................................................................................................................

......................................................................................................................

......................................................................................................................

......................................................................................................................

......................................................................................................................

......................................................................................................................

......................................................................................................................

......................................................................................................................

......................................................................................................................

......................................................................................................................

......................................................................................................................

......................................................................................................................

......................................................................................................................

......................................................................................................................

......................................................................................................................

......................................................................................................................

......................................................................................................................

......................................................................................................................

......................................................................................................................

......................................................................................................................

MS-LS2-1, MS-LS2-3, MS-ESS3-1,
EP&CIc, EP&CIIb, EP&CIIIa

## Inquiry

- How can we use interactions between individual rocks or individual organisms to understand systems as big as the whole geosphere or whole ecosystem?
- How can we use patterns in geosphere interactions to predict the location of resources?
- How can we use patterns in ecosystem interactions to predict how organisms compete and share resources?

## Topics

### Before the Topics
### Identify the Problem

# Gold Mining and California Ecosystems

**Phenomenon** On January 24, 1848, a carpenter named James W. Marshall came upon a nugget of gold in Sutter Creek in the Sierra Nevada foothills. News of Marshall's find spread quickly, sparking what would come to be known as the California Gold Rush. The valuable metal has been mined in the state ever since. Riches have been made, but mining has also had serious negative effects on the ecosystems of California.

Following the discovery of gold, thousands of people flocked to the "Gold Country" of California to seek their fortunes. Gold fields were primarily located around Coloma, in the northeastern part of the state, and between Yreka and Shasta, in the northern part of the state.

# Geology of a Gold Rush

Gold is a mineral that can be found all over Earth. In most places, it exists only as very small specks mixed in with much larger amounts of rock and other minerals. For this reason, looking for gold in most places is not worth the effort. In some places, however, geological forces concentrate gold in larger amounts and place it closer to the surface. California happens to be one of those places.

Earth's crust is broken up into pieces called plates. California sits at the meeting point of the Pacific Plate and the North American Plate. These plates are sliding past each other, with parts of the Pacific Plate slowly sinking under the North American Plate. This interaction is responsible for volcanic activity and the formation of mountain ranges parallel to the coast. As molten rock moves from Earth's interior toward the surface, it picks up particles of minerals and metals, including gold. As the molten rock cools, minerals in it crystalize into veins of rock, called quartz. The deposits of gold remain trapped inside the quartz. Over time, some of these rocks weather and erode. The gold gets carried away by streams and rivers. Other gold deposits remain trapped in rock. California gold miners eventually found ways to remove these deposits.

Large flecks of gold are visible in this quartz rock.

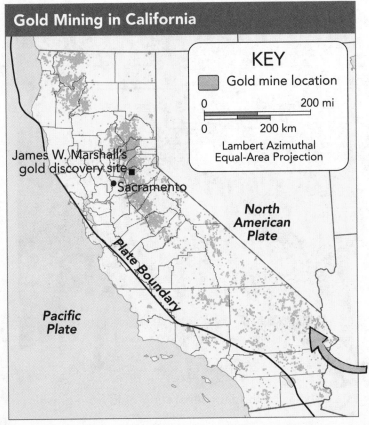

**Gold Mining in California**

KEY

Gold mine location

| 0 | 200 mi |
| 0 | 200 km |

Lambert Azimuthal Equal-Area Projection

James W. Marshall's gold discovery site

Sacramento

North American Plate

Plate Boundary

Pacific Plate

Gold was found throughout California, with the greatest concentrations in a few regions.

1. **SEP Use Models** On the map, circle two areas where gold mining was most concentrated.

2. **CCC Cause and Effect** Why are there more mining sites in these areas than in other parts of California?

..........................................................
..........................................................
..........................................................
..........................................................
..........................................................

# Early Mining Methods

The earliest California miners mostly found gold by panning for it. They sifted through the sediment in the bottom of rivers, using a pan that was shaped like a pie plate. They then used the running water to help them separate any gold from the rest of the small bits of rock. The water helped to clean away dust from the sediment so miners could see what they had. After rinsing and separating, miners sometimes found a few small nuggets of gold. Often they found nothing. Panning was physically difficult work, and it rarely yielded significant amounts of gold.

To increase efficiency, some miners used sluice boxes to help them sift through more sediment. The sluice box worked using the same principles as panning. River water was poured through the sluice. Gold settled to the bottom and the rest of the sediment was washed away.

These processes left a great deal of environmental damage in their wake. They disturbed riverbeds and stirred up sediment in rivers. As a result, aquatic plants suffered from a lack of sunlight, and so did the organisms in these ecosystems that relied on these plants for food and shelter. However, the impact of these methods on California ecosystems was minimal compared to what miners would later do as gold became more difficult to extract.

These gold nuggets were discovered in a river in California. They have been made smooth by the running water.

Sluicing was a popular method for separating gold from gravel in California.

# Hydraulic Mining

Eventually, miners figured out that the source of the gold they were finding in rivers was the steep cliffs of loose gravel along the rivers. To get at this gold, mining companies began to use a system called hydraulic mining, which used high-pressure hoses to shoot water at the cliffs. The gravel broke up and washed away. Then, the gravel and water moved through sluices that separated the gold from other sediments.

Hydraulic mining was an efficient way to mine gold, but it also caused significant damage to California ecosystems. Leftover sediment was dumped into nearby rivers and streams, many of which had already been damaged by people panning for gold. Some rivers became so clogged with sediment that fish could not swim in them anymore. As a result, many water and wetland habitats were gravely harmed or disappeared completely. The buildup of sediment and the resulting floods affected farmers and towns downstream as well. In 1884, after an outcry from farmers and other concerned citizens, the state outlawed the dumping of mining debris in rivers.

Hydraulic mining relied on pressurized water to break up gravel so gold could be separated from it.

**Compare and Contrast** 🖊 Complete the Venn diagram to compare and contrast hydraulic mining with earlier mining methods.

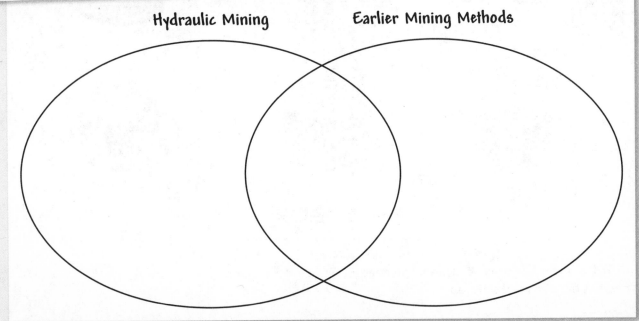

Hydraulic Mining          Earlier Mining Methods

# Mercury Contamination

Miners were also eager to remove gold from hard veins of quartz even farther up in the mountains. This type of mining, which is called hard rock mining, was particularly challenging. In these areas, gold was stuck inside solid rock. To get at the gold, miners dynamited the rock and then ground it into a fine powder. Then, they used mercury to help separate the gold from the sediments. It was a groundbreaking feat of engineering. However, mercury is toxic. It causes brain and nerve damage in most living things. Mercury absorbed by plants eventually finds it way into other organisms in an ecosystem. Mercury hasn't been used in mining since the 1960s. Yet, even today, many old mines in California and the waterways near them are not safe to visit because of mercury contamination.

In this segment, you will learn about the distribution of natural resources on Earth and the factors that affect this distribution. You will also learn how living things interact with each other in ecosystems. As you read the topics, think about how our use of natural resources impacts ecosystems and what we can do to maintain healthy ecosystems.

Mining companies relied on a process that used mercury to remove gold from rock.

Gold stuck in rocks

② .................................

Mercury

① .................................

③ .................................

⑥ .................................

⑤ .................................

④ .................................

**SEP Develop Models** 🖊 Under the images, write a description of what happens at each step.

# Distribution of Natural Resources

**Investigative Phenomenon**
How can you explain the uneven distributions of Earth's natural resources?

**MS-ESS3-1** Construct a scientific explanation based on evidence for how the uneven distributions of Earth's mineral, energy, and groundwater resources are the result of past and current geoscience processes.

**EP&CIc** Students should be developing an understanding that the quality, quantity, and reliability of the goods and ecosystem services provided by natural systems are directly affected by the health of those systems.

**HOW** did this gold get in this rock?

**HANDS-ON LAB**

иConnect Observe coal to draw conclusions about its formation.

What questions do you have about the phenomenon?

..........................................................................................................
..........................................................................................................
..........................................................................................................
..........................................................................................................
..........................................................................................................
..........................................................................................................
..........................................................................................................
..........................................................................................................
..........................................................................................................
..........................................................................................................

MS-ESS3-1 Construct a scientific explanation based on evidence for how the uneven distributions of Earth's mineral, energy, and groundwater resources are the result of past and current geoscience processes. (Also **EP&CIc**)

## Connect It!

✏️ **Identify and label some the materials that are being used in this construction project.**

Classify Pick one of the materials you identified in the photo and explain whether you think the resource is limited or unlimited.

...........................................................................................................................

...........................................................................................................................

9th St

# Natural Resources

We all rely on natural resources to live and work (**Figure 1**). A **natural resource** is anything occuring naturally in the environment that humans use. We need air to breathe, water to drink, soil in which to grow plants to eat, sunlight to make those plants grow, and other natural resources. Some of these resources are essentially unlimited and renewable regardless of what we do. For example, sunlight and wind are available daily at most places on Earth. Other renewable resources can be reused or replenished, but it may require some care or planning. For example, wood from trees is a renewable resource as long as some trees are spared to reproduce and make the next generation of trees.

Other resources are **nonrenewable resources,** which cannot be replaced. This may be because there is a finite amount of the resource on Earth and we don't have a way to make more of it. The element silver, for example, cannot be made from other substances. The amount of silver on Earth is set. Other resources are considered nonrenewable because it takes very long periods of time for them to form.

✓ CHECK POINT **Cite Evidence** Why is wood considered to be a renewable resource?

.................................................................................................

.................................................................................................

.................................................................................................

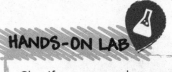
**HANDS-ON LAB**

Classify resources that you use in a typical day.

📖**Reflect** In your science notebook, describe how a natural resource could shift from being renewable to nonrenewable.

**Resource Use**
**Figure 1** This construction project in Los Angeles, California, relies on a number of natural resources.

# Fossil Fuels

The sources of energy commonly called fossil fuels include coal, petroleum, and natural gas. **Fossil fuels** are the energy-rich substances made from the preserved remains of organisms. The chemical energy in fossil fuels can be converted to other forms by burning them.

The energy stored in these compounds originally arrived on Earth as sunlight. Photosynthetic organisms such as algae, moss, grasses, and trees converted sunlight into carbon-based compounds. When animals ate the plants, they absorbed some of those compounds. Under certain conditions involving high temperatures and pressures, the remains of these organisms were transformed into new materials, including solid coal, liquid petroleum, and methane gas.

**Coal** Coal is formed from the remains of plants that died long ago in and around swampy areas. There are different grades, or types, of coal (**Figure 2**). Each grade forms under different conditions, as shown in **Figure 3**. In addition to being a source of energy, coal is used in a wide array of applications. Coal is used in water and air purification systems, as well as medical equipment such as kidney dialysis devices. Coal is used to make steel from iron ore.

Burning coal in coal-fired power plants accounts for about 30 percent of the electricity produced in the United States. Coal has long been used as a fuel because it has twice as much energy per unit of mass as wood. So, when coal can be mined at a large scale, it can be an efficient source of energy.

Unfortunately, burning coal produces pollutants and causes millions of deaths each year from health problems. Coal mining also requires large mines to be dug into the ground, or the removal of mountaintops or other surface layers to access coal beds. Removing coal causes great damage to the surrounding environment, threatening other types of natural resources and the ecosystem services they provide.

☑ CHECK POINT **Determine Central Ideas** What is the original source of the energy contained in coal? Explain.

....................................................................................................

....................................................................................................

....................................................................................................

Lignite

Bituminous Coal

Anthracite

## Types of Coal

**Figure 2** Brittle, lustrous anthracite has more energy than crumbly, dull lignite.

**Determine Differences** Why might one type of coal contain more energy than another type of coal?

....................................................

....................................................

....................................................

....................................................

## Coal Formation and Distribution

**Figure 3** Coal only forms under the right conditions. The map shows major deposits of coal around the world.

1. **SEP Use Models** ✏ Circle the three continents that have the most coal resources.

2. **SEP Construct Explanations** Why is coal not evenly distributed around the world?

..............................................................

..............................................................

..............................................................

..............................................................

**KEY**

◼ Coal deposit

Swamp Environment

**PEAT**
(Partially altered plant material; very smoky when burned, low energy)

Burial

Compaction

**LIGNITE**
(Soft, brown coal; moderate energy)

Greater burial

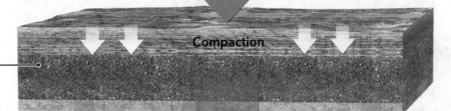

Compaction

**BITUMINOUS COAL**
(Soft, black coal; major coal used in power generation and industry; high energy)

Metamorphism

**ANTHRACITE**
(Hard, black coal; used in industry; highest energy)

Stress

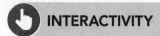
**INTERACTIVITY**

Explore the distribution of different fossil fuels.

**VIDEO**

Learn more about how fossil fuels form underground.

**Oil** What we commonly refer to as oil is scientifically known as **petroleum**, from the Latin terms *petra* (rock) and *oleum* (oil). Petroleum is made of the remains of small animals, algae, and other organisms that lived in marine environments hundreds of millions of years ago. Oil deposits form when these remains become trapped underground and are subject to high pressure and temperature.

Because it is a liquid and can be processed into different fuels, petroleum is especially useful for powering engines in automobiles, ships, trains, and airplanes. Petroleum also has many important industrial uses, such as making plastics, lubricants, and fertilizers. Petroleum is also the basis for synthetic fibers, such as rayon, carbon fiber, and nylon. Many cosmetic and pharmaceutical products, such as petroleum jelly and tar shampoos that treat dandruff, contain forms of petroleum.

As with coal, burning oil and natural gas emits carbon dioxide. Oil can also be spilled, which can be disastrous for wildlife and water quality (**Figure 4**). Natural gas leaks contribute to global warming, and can result in explosions if the concentration of gas is high and a spark ignites it.

**Oil Impacts**

**Figure 4** Oil is often drilled from the ocean floor and transported by ship. Major oil spills can harm or kill wildlife, as well as damage habitats and water quality.

1. SEP Interpret Data  What are the two major causes of accidental oil spills?

.................................................................................

2. SEP Use Mathematics  About how much more oil was spilled as a result of the Deepwater Horizon explosion than the *Valdez* running aground?

.................................................................................

| Location and Date | Amount Spilled (gallons) | Cause |
|---|---|---|
| Santa Barbara, California, 1969 | 4 million | Blown-out offshore oil drilling platform |
| Trinidad and Tobago, 1979 | 90 million | Collision of two oil tanker ships |
| Gulf of Mexico, 1979 | 140 million | Blown-out *Ixtoc 1* oil well on ocean floor, fire, collapse of drilling platform |
| Persian Gulf, 1983 | 80 million | Collision of ship with oil-drilling platform during Iraq-Iran war |
| Prince William Sound, Alaska, 1989 | 11 million | *Exxon Valdez* oil tanker ship runs aground, puncturing hull |
| Gulf of Mexico, 2010 | 181 million | Blown-out Deepwater Horizon oil well, explosion of platform |

## Petroleum Formation and Distribution

**Figure 5** Petroleum has been drilled for all over the world. Wells or rigs are constructed to tap "fields" of oil hundreds or thousands of meters below Earth's surface, both on land and water.

**SEP Engage in Argument** 🖊 A large sea once existed in the United States. Shade the area of the country where you think the sea likely existed. Then explain your choice.

...........................................................................................

...........................................................................................

...........................................................................................

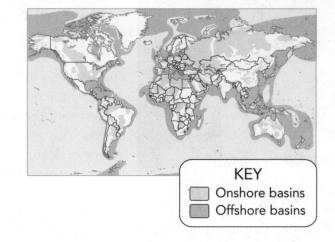

KEY
☐ Onshore basins
☐ Offshore basins

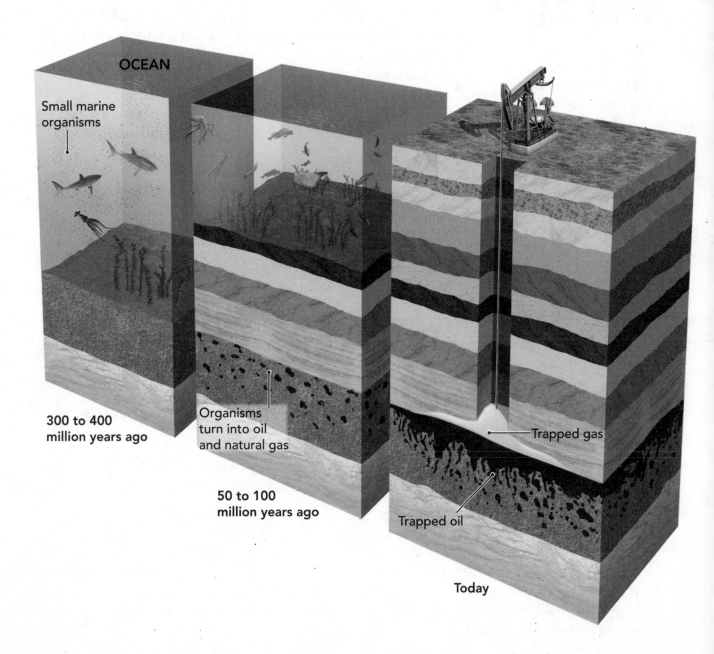

OCEAN

Small marine organisms

**300 to 400 million years ago**

Organisms turn into oil and natural gas

**50 to 100 million years ago**

Trapped gas

Trapped oil

**Today**

15

## Fracking

**Figure 6** Groundwater samples taken from sites where fracking has occurred have tested positive for methane and other hydrocarbons.

**Natural Gas** Formed from the same processes that produce oil and found in the same locations, natural gas is trapped in pockets within layers of rock deep below Earth's surface. A drill can tap the trapped gas, and then pipelines carry the gas for processing and transport. Burning petroleum and coal releases more carbon dioxide than burning natural gas. This is one reason many countries have encouraged more use of natural gas and are surveying underground basins of gas for further exploitation. On the other hand, the gas itself is a powerful greenhouse gas that contributes to global warming. This means any leaks of natural gas from wells, pipelines, and other structures pose a significant pollution problem.

To meet the demand for natural gas, a process called *fracking* has become popular. Fracking, which works for both oil and gas, is short for hydraulic fracturing. This involves using pressured fluids to break layers of shale rock and force out the trapped natural gas, which can then be collected and transported. There are concerns that the fracking fluids are contaminating vital stores of groundwater that humans rely on (**Figure 6**) and natural systems whose health is important to human activities.

✓ CHECK POINT **Cite Textual Evidence** Natural gas burns cleaner than coal, yet it is considered a pollutant. Why?

........................................................................................

........................................................................................

## Math Toolbox

### Natural Gas Consumption in the U.S.

In recent years, consumption patterns of natural gas have changed.

1. **SEP Use Mathematics** What was the percent increase in gas usage from 1980 to 2015? Show your work.

........................................................................................

........................................................................................

2. **Analyze Relationships** What trend is shown in the data?

........................................................................................

........................................................................................

3. **CCC Cause and Effect** What factors contributed to the trend shown in the data?

........................................................................................

........................................................................................

| U.S. Annual Natural Gas Consumption | |
|---|---|
| Year | Volume (Million Cubic Meters) |
| 1980 | 562,862 |
| 1985 | 489,342 |
| 1990 | 542,935 |
| 1995 | 628,829 |
| 2000 | 660,720 |
| 2005 | 623,379 |
| 2010 | 682,062 |
| 2015 | 773,228 |

Source: U.S. Energy Information Administration

# Nuclear Energy

Nuclear power is another nonrenewable energy resource used to generate much of the world's electricity. Nuclear energy provides 20 percent of the electricity in the United States. Inside a nuclear power plant, controlled nuclear fission reactions occur. **Nuclear fission** is the splitting of an atom's nucleus into two nuclei. Fission releases a great deal of energy. This energy is used to heat water, turning it into steam. The steam is then used to turn the blades of a turbine to produce electricity.

Uranium is the fuel used for nuclear fission inside nuclear reactors. It is a heavy metal that occurs in most rocks and is usually extracted through mining. The uranium found on Earth was part of the original cloud of dust and gas from which our solar system formed. Uranium is found throughout Earth's crust. But large ores of the material are formed from geological processes that only occur in certain locations on Earth (**Figure 7**).

## Literacy Connection

**Cite Textual Evidence** As you read, underline text that supports the idea that uranium is a limited resource with finite amounts on Earth.

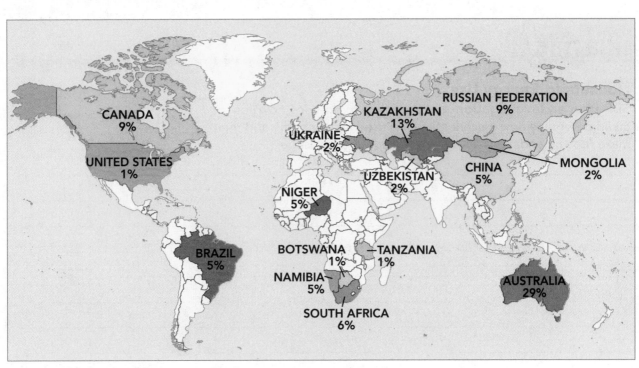

Source: World Nuclear Association

## Distribution of Uranium

**Figure 7** According to the World Nuclear Association, almost 70 percent of accessible uranium is found in only 5 countries.

1. **SEP Use Models** ✏ Circle the two countries with the greatest percentage of uranium resources.

2. **CCC Patterns** What patterns do you observe in the distribution of uranium?

......................................................................................................

......................................................................................................

......................................................................................................

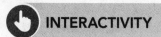

**INTERACTIVITY**

Learn more about the progression of living matter to petroleum.

# Using Energy Resources

Fossil fuels are among the most important nonrenewable resources for humans. As the human population has grown, these resources have become less abundant. Geologists estimate that we have already used about half the petroleum that fossilization, pressure, heat, and time have produced over hundreds of millions of years—and all in just a few centuries.

**Pollution** Humans are burning fossil fuels at a faster rate than the resulting carbon emissions can be absorbed by natural processes, such as photosynthesis. This is why the concentration of carbon dioxide in the atmosphere is now 45 percent higher than it was just over 200 years ago. Scientists have concluded that this is fueling global warming and climate change.

## Plan It

### Household Energy Use

**SEP Plan an Investigation** Use the space to describe how you could determine how much fossil fuel is used in your home and then make recommendations about how to reduce your usage.

........................................................................................................................

........................................................................................................................

........................................................................................................................

........................................................................................................................

........................................................................................................................

........................................................................................................................

........................................................................................................................

........................................................................................................................

........................................................................................................................

........................................................................................................................

........................................................................................................................

........................................................................................................................

........................................................................................................................

........................................................................................................................

........................................................................................................................

........................................................................................................................

**World Politics** The uneven distribution of fossil fuel resources has led to political problems, including war. In 1990, Iraq invaded neighboring Kuwait in part because of disagreements over how oil fields at a shared border should be used. When the United States and other nations came to Kuwait's defense and drove out the Iraqi forces, oil fields and wells were set on fire. This resulted in hundreds of millions of gallons of oil being burned or spilled, and untreated emissions billowing into the atmosphere (**Figure 8**).

☑CHECK POINT **Determine Conclusions** How have human activities affected the distribution of fossil fuels on Earth?

........................................................................................................

........................................................................................................

........................................................................................................

........................................................................................................

........................................................................................................

### Gulf War Oil Fires

**Figure 8** The oil fields that were set on fire during the first Gulf War in 1991 caused significant damage to the land and living things.

# ☑ LESSON 1 Check

MS-ESS3-1, EP&CIc

**1. Identify** Which fossil fuel is produced from the remains of peat?

......................................................................

**2. CCC Cause and Effect** A friend argues that the location of a petroleum deposit is a sign that marine organisms once lived there. Is your friend correct? Explain.

......................................................................

......................................................................

......................................................................

......................................................................

......................................................................

......................................................................

......................................................................

**3. Apply Scientific Reasoning** How does the abundance of a resource, and whether it is renewable or nonrenewable, affect how much it is used?

......................................................................

......................................................................

......................................................................

......................................................................

......................................................................

......................................................................

......................................................................

......................................................................

......................................................................

......................................................................

......................................................................

**4. SEP Engage in Argument** What advantage does coal have over wood as an energy source? What is the major disadvantage of using coal for energy?

......................................................................

......................................................................

......................................................................

......................................................................

......................................................................

......................................................................

......................................................................

......................................................................

......................................................................

......................................................................

**5. SEP Construct Explanations** Why are oil, coal, and natural gas not found evenly distributed on Earth?

......................................................................

......................................................................

......................................................................

......................................................................

......................................................................

......................................................................

......................................................................

......................................................................

......................................................................

......................................................................

......................................................................

# Micro-Hydro
# POWER

▶ VIDEO

Examine how hydroelectric power plants and wind farms generate clean energy.

**How can people without** access to electricity use moving water to generate power? You engineer it!

**The Challenge:** To generate power from moving water.

Earth's water system is an excellent source of power. Centuries ago, people realized that moving water, properly channeled, can turn wheels that make machinery move. More recently, engineers designed large-scale dams to harness the energy of moving water. Water power's great advantage is that the water is always moving, so electricity can be generated 24 hours a day.

Now engineers have developed hydropower on a small scale, known as micro-hydro power. If there is a small river or stream running through your property, then you need only a few basic things: a turbine, pipes to channel the water to the turbine, and a generator that will transform the energy into electricity.

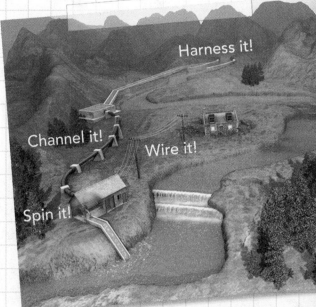

Harness it!

Channel it!

Wire it!

Spin it!

In this micro-hydro system, water from the river is channeled to the generator, which transforms the energy of the moving water into electrical energy.

## DESIGN CHALLENGE

Can you design a micro-hydro system? Go to the Engineering Design Notebook to find out!

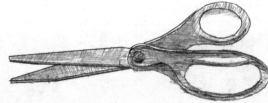

# Mineral Resources

**иInvestigate** Explore the geological processes that form minerals.

**MS-ESS3-1** Construct a scientific explanation based on evidence for how the uneven distributions of Earth's mineral, energy, and groundwater resources are the result of past and current geoscience processes. (Also **EP&CIc**)

## Connect It!

✏️ **Circle some of the objects in the photo that you think contain minerals.**

SEP Construct Explanations  How do you think these minerals formed?

.............................................................................................................

.............................................................................................................

.............................................................................................................

# Minerals and Ores

You may think that minerals are only found in rocks. It's true that rocks are made from minerals, but if you look around, you will probably see many other things that are made from minerals. Metals are made from one or more minerals. The graphite in a pencil is a type of mineral. Computers, smartphones, and other electronic devices are made with metals and other minerals, too. Even you contain minerals, such as the calcium-bearing minerals that make up your bones and teeth.

But what is a mineral? A mineral is a solid substance that is non-living and made from a particular combination of elements. There are over 5,000 named minerals on Earth. Gold, quartz, and talc are just a few examples. When a mixture of a mineral and the surrounding rock is large enough and valuable enough for it to be extracted from the ground, it is known as **ore**. People remove ore from the ground and refine it, a process that separates the minerals from the rock. They can then use or sell the minerals to make money.

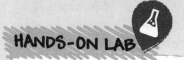

## HANDS-ON LAB

**Investigate** Explore the geological processes that form minerals.

**Reflect** Throughout the day, list some of the things you see and use that are made from minerals. Then, at the end of the day, write a paragraph explaining why minerals are important and describing some of their most important uses.

## Stalactite Formation

**Figure 1** These stalactites in Carlsbad Caverns National Park in New Mexico formed as minerals deposited by a dripping mineral-rich solution built up over long periods of time.

**Determine Meaning**

As you read, circle or underline an unknown word in the text and use context clues to help you determine the meaning. Revisit the unknown word at the end of the lesson and use a resource if you still cannot determine the meaning.

**How Minerals Form** Minerals form in different ways. They can form from organic materials, from mineral-rich solutions, and from cooling magma and lava.

**Organic Material** Corals like the ones in **Figure 2** create a hard outer skeleton that provides the coral with shape and protection. This skeleton is made from thin layers of calcium carbonate (also called the mineral calcite), a chemical compound similar to the shells of other sea animals. Once the coral is dead, the calcium carbonate skeleton is left behind. It may get buried and broken down into smaller fragments.

### Minerals from Living Things

**Figure 2** These corals produce a hard outer skeleton made from the mineral calcite. The skeleton will be around for a long time after the coral dies.

Apply Concepts Why wouldn't other body parts of living things, such as skin, become minerals after an organism's death?

.................................................................................................................

.................................................................................................................

**Solutions** When water contains dissolved substances it is called a solution. In some cases, the substances in these solutions will **crystallize** to form a new mineral. This can happen within bodies of water and underground. One way this happens on Earth's surface involves the process of evaporation. When the water evaporates, the elements and compounds that are left behind crystallize into new minerals such as salts. This is how the mineral formations in **Figure 3** formed.

Another way that minerals form from solutions is through a process in which a warm solution flows through a crack in existing rock. Elements and compounds leave the solution as it cools and crystallize as minerals in the crack. These form veins of ores that are different from the surrounding rock.

**Magma and Lava** The molten and semi-molten rock mixture found beneath Earth's surface is known as magma. In its molten, or melted state, magma is very hot. But when it cools, it hardens into solid rock. This rock is made from crystallized minerals. It may form beneath Earth's surface or above Earth's surface when magma (which is known as lava when it breaks the surface) erupts from the ground and then cools and hardens as is shown in **Figure 4.**

The types of minerals that form from magma and lava vary based on the materials and gases in the magma, as well as the rate at which it cools.

☑CHECK POINT **Analyze Text Structure** Examine the way the text on these two pages has been organized. Describe how the author has organized the text so that it supports the reader's comprehension.

..............................................................................

..............................................................................

..............................................................................

..............................................................................

..............................................................................

**Minerals from Solutions**
**Figure 3** These mineral deposits in Mammoth Hot Springs in Yellowstone National Park formed from a solution.

SEP Analyze Data 🖊 Draw an X on the solution the minerals formed from. Circle some of the mineral deposits.

**Minerals from Magma**
**Figure 4** As this lava cools, it will harden and crystallize into minerals.

CCC Cause and Effect Where would you expect to find minerals that have formed in this way?

..............................................................................

..............................................................................

**Gold Rush**

**Figure 5** California's geological history produced mineral-rich rock and soil. The discovery of gold in the state resulted in the Gold Rush of 1849.

**Academic Vocabulary**

Explain what *distributed* means and give one or two examples of something that is distributed.

.................................................

.................................................

.................................................

## Distribution of Minerals

The distribution of mineral resources on Earth depends on how and when the minerals form. Common minerals, such as the ones that make up most of the rocks in Earth's crust, are found roughly evenly distributed around the planet. Other minerals are rare because they only form as a result of tremendous heat and pressure near volcanic systems. Therefore, these minerals will only be found near subduction zones or other regions associated with volcanic activity. Other minerals may form from evaporation in the ocean or on land, such as in basins called playas. The map in **Figure 6** shows how some minerals are **distributed** around the world.

Gold, for example, is a heavy metal that formed, along with all other atoms other than hydrogen and helium, from stars that went supernova preceding the formation of our solar system. Gold is rare at the surface because most of it sank into the core when the early Earth was molten. Gold gets concentrated when hot fluids pass through the crust and pick up the gold, which doesn't fit well in the crystals of most rocks.

☑ CHECK POINT **Determine Meaning** Locate the term *concentrated* in the second paragraph. Using context clues, what do you think this word means? Explain your thinking.

.................................................................................

.................................................................................

.................................................................................

# Question It!

**Minerals for Dinner?**

Minerals are used in many ways in our everyday lives. We even need minerals in our diets to stay healthy. Humans need minerals that contain calcium, potassium, and magnesium to grow, fight illness, and carry out everyday functions.

**Apply Scientific Reasoning** Write two or three questions you would like to have answered about the importance of minerals in your diet.

.....................................................................

.....................................................................

.....................................................................

.....................................................................

.....................................................................

.....................................................................

.....................................................................

.....................................................................

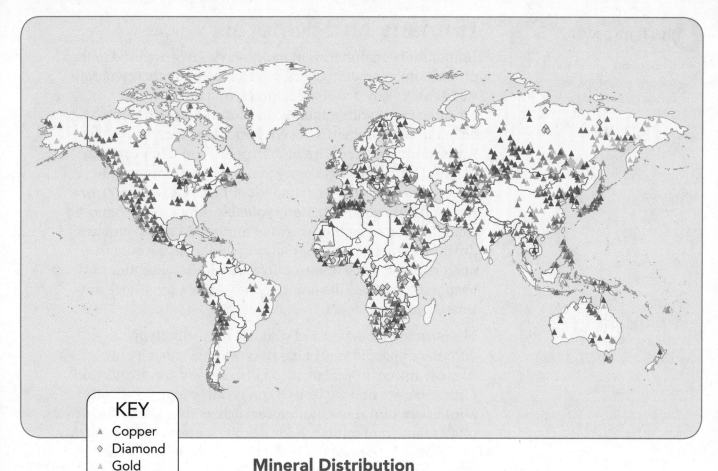

**KEY**
- ▲ Copper
- ◇ Diamond
- ▲ Gold
- ▲ Iron
- ▲ Lead-Zinc
- ▲ Silver
- △ Uranium

## INTERACTIVITY

Find out more about mineral resources and their distributions.

## VIDEO

Learn why some minerals are only found in certain places.

## Mineral Distribution

**Figure 6** Minerals are distributed unevenly on Earth.

1. **Claim** Which part of the United States is the richest in gold and other mineral resources?

.................................................................

2. **Evidence** ✏ Circle the area on the map that provides evidence to support your claim.

3. **Reasoning** Suppose you were to draw the boundaries of tectonic plates and locations of volcanic activity on the map. What patterns would you notice among plate boundaries, volcanic activity, and the distribution of different mineral resources? How do these patterns relate to California's mineral resources? Explain.

.................................................................
.................................................................
.................................................................
.................................................................
.................................................................
.................................................................
.................................................................
.................................................................
.................................................................

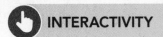

**INTERACTIVITY**

Explore the use of the mineral limestone as a building material.

# Humans and Minerals

Humans rely on minerals in many ways. They are used in the production of buildings, cars, electronics, and other materials we use every day. Jewelry, sculpture, and other works of art are often made with minerals, such as marble, jade, and emerald. Some minerals are easy and inexpensive to get. For instance, bananas are high in potassium. They are also plentiful, affordable, and easy to find in any grocery store. Other minerals, such as diamonds or benitoite (**Figure 7**), are rare and difficult to get. Many valuable minerals are removed from the ground by the process of mining. As more minerals are mined, there are fewer places to find them because they are a nonrenewable resource. In other words, once they have been removed from the ground, they will not grow back any time soon.

The push to find deposits of valuable minerals often encourages people to take big risks. Mining can not only damage the environment, it can also be very dangerous work. Mine collapses and explosions can result in injury or death. Mining can also result in illnesses such as "black lung," which affects some coal miners. Additionally, some valuable minerals are located in parts of the world that are politically unstable. When companies attempt to mine for these minerals there, it can cause problems and danger for everyone involved.

✓ CHECK POINT **Summarize Text** How do humans rely on minerals?

.............................................................................................................

.............................................................................................................

.............................................................................................................

## Rare Mineral

**Figure 7** Benitoite is a very rare blue mineral that forms as a result of hydrothermal processes in Earth's crust. It has been discovered in a few locations on Earth. But gemstone-quality benitoite can be found in only one place in California.

**Connect to Society**
Do you think a benitoite ring would be costly or inexpensive? Explain your reasoning.

.........................................................

.........................................................

.........................................................

.........................................................

.........................................................

.........................................................

# ☑ LESSON 2 Check

MS-ESS3-1, EP&Clc

**1. Define** What are minerals? List examples.

........................................................................

........................................................................

........................................................................

........................................................................

........................................................................

........................................................................

........................................................................

........................................................................

**2. SEP Construct Explanations** Explain the relationship between minerals and ores.

........................................................................

........................................................................

........................................................................

........................................................................

........................................................................

........................................................................

........................................................................

........................................................................

........................................................................

........................................................................

**3. CCC Cause and Effect** What causes minerals to be unevenly distributed on Earth?

........................................................................

........................................................................

........................................................................

........................................................................

........................................................................

........................................................................

........................................................................

........................................................................

........................................................................

........................................................................

**4. CCC Patterns** ✏ Use drawings to show one of the ways that minerals can form.

# (3) Water Resources

## HANDS-ON LAB

**uInvestigate** Model how an artesian well accesses groundwater.

**MS-ESS3-1** Construct a scientific explanation based on evidence for how the uneven distributions of Earth's mineral, energy, and groundwater resources are the result of past and current geoscience processes. (Also **EP&Clc**)

## Connect It !

✏️ **The drop of water on Earth represents all the water on the planet. Draw a circle inside the drop of water to represent the amount of fresh water you think exists on Earth.**

**CCC Systems** How does water's role in Earth systems make it an important natural resource?

.......................................................................................................................

.......................................................................................................................

.......................................................................................................................

# Water on Earth

Although Earth is known as the water planet, the water that living things rely on represents only a fraction of the planet's total water supply **(Figure 1)**. Most water on Earth is salt water. Fresh water is only found on the surface of our planet as surface ice or water, or within Earth's crust as groundwater.

Water is a limited resource, which means there is a finite amount of it on Earth. In addition, it is not evenly distributed around the planet as a result of meteorological and geological forces. The water cycle circulates water through Earth's ocean and other bodies of water, on and below its surface, and in the atmosphere. A very small amount of the water on the surface of the planet is immediately available for human use in lakes and rivers, but most fresh water is locked up as ice at the poles and in glaciers.

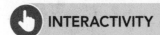

## INTERACTIVITY

Predict how much water on Earth is drinkable.

**Reflect** How is water used in your local environment? In your science notebook, describe some ways your local environment would be affected if there were suddenly less water available.

## A Drop to Drink

**Figure 1** If all of the water on Earth were collected, it would form a sphere about 1,380 kilometers (860 miles) across.

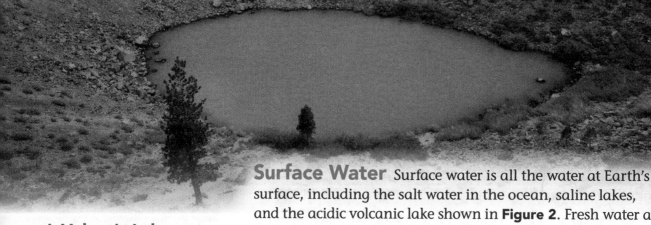

## A Volcanic Lake

**Figure 2** The Inyo craters are a series of volcanic craters in eastern California. Small lakes have formed in some of these craters.

**SEP Construct Explanations** How do you think the water ended up in the lake?

....................................................

....................................................

....................................................

....................................................

**Surface Water** Surface water is all the water at Earth's surface, including the salt water in the ocean, saline lakes, and the acidic volcanic lake shown in **Figure 2**. Fresh water at Earth's surface is found as moisture on top of the soil. In colder regions, this water remains frozen as permafrost. Most fresh water at the surface is found in lakes, rivers, and streams, as well as swamps and marshes. These sources of water are not evenly distributed across Earth. Precipitation, which depends on factors such as atmospheric patterns and temperature, determines where surface water forms.

Most of the fresh water at Earth's surface is found in lakes. Lakes form through various geological processes when water fills in depressions in Earth's surface. These can occur as a result of erosion, the movement of tectonic plates, and retreating glaciers. Some lakes form when a river's path erodes away an area or a dam blocks a river's flow. All rivers begin as a small flow of water caused by gravity. Runoff from rain or melting ice collects and flows downhill following the least resistant path. These small flows of water form streams, which combine and grow to form larger rivers and river systems.

# Math Toolbox

## Distribution of Water Resources

While most of the planet is covered in water, only a small amount of it is available to humans for cooking, drinking, and bathing.

1. **SEP Develop Models** Use the data in the graphs to complete the missing values.

2. **Draw Comparative Inferences** About how much more accessible surface fresh water is found in lakes than in the atmosphere as water vapor?

....................................................

....................................................

....................................................

....................................................

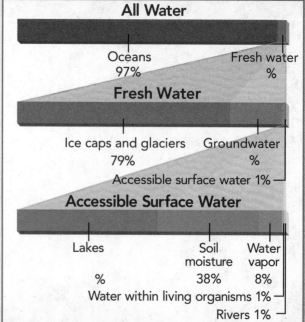

### Distribution of the World's Water

**All Water**

Oceans 97%   Fresh water %

**Fresh Water**

Ice caps and glaciers 79%   Groundwater %

Accessible surface water 1%

**Accessible Surface Water**

Lakes %   Soil moisture 38%   Water vapor 8%

Water within living organisms 1%

Rivers 1%

## Groundwater

**Groundwater** As with fresh water at the surface, groundwater is not evenly distributed across Earth **(Figure 3)**. The presence of groundwater depends on the type of rock layers in Earth's crust. Groundwater forms when gravity causes water from precipitation and runoff to seep into the ground and fill the empty spaces between these rocks. Some rocks are more porous, or have more empty spaces in which water can collect. The volume of porous rock that can contain groundwater is called an aquifer. Wells are drilled into aquifers to access the water.

Deep groundwater reservoirs can take hundreds or thousands of years to accumulate, especially in arid regions where there is little rainfall or surface water to supply the aquifer. New studies of Earth's mantle reveal there may be many oceans' worth of water locked hundreds of kilometers below the surface in mineral formations. This groundwater may take millions of years to exchange with surface water through the movement of tectonic plates and mantle convection.

**CHECK POINT** **Summarize** How does the type of rock in Earth's crust affect the distribution of groundwater?

.........................................................................................................

.........................................................................................................

.........................................................................................................

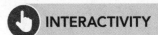
**INTERACTIVITY**

Explore how groundwater is distributed around Earth.

HANDS-ON LAB

**Investigate** Model how an artesian well accesses groundwater.

### Distribution of Groundwater

**Figure 3** Groundwater is especially important in areas that do not have immediate access to rivers or lakes for sources of fresh water.

**SEP Use Models** Indicate the areas on the map with the greatest groundwater resources with a circle. Indicate the areas with the least groundwater resources with an X.

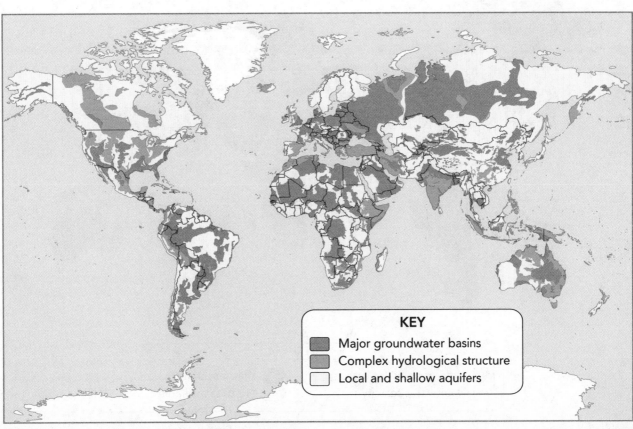

KEY
- Major groundwater basins
- Complex hydrological structure
- Local and shallow aquifers

**Literacy Connection**

**Support Author's Claim** Underline the text that supports the claim that human activity can cause water shortages.

# Human Impacts

Humans rely on water not only to live and grow, but also for agriculture and industry. Water is needed to produce our food, manufacture products, and carry out many chemical reactions. The distribution of water resources is a result of past and current geologic processes such as the water cycle, plate tectonics, and the formation of rock. These processes take time, and in some areas humans are depleting water resources faster than they can be replenished. The human impact on water distribution is already a cause of social and economic conflict in some areas.

**Using Water** Humans use surface water, which often involves changing its natural path, such as with dams. This affects the amount of water that continues to flow and the ecology of the area. Humans access groundwater resources by digging wells in aquifers. But if more water is removed from an aquifer or other groundwater source than is replenished through the water cycle, water shortages can occur, such as the drought that affected California from 2011 through 2016. As with surface water, pollution can enter groundwater supplies and impact the quality of the water. Study the effects of water scarcity in **Figure 4.**

## Water Scarcity

**Figure 4** Many people and regions will be affected by water scarcity in the future.

**CCC Cause and Effect** How might water scarcity affect economic development in an area?

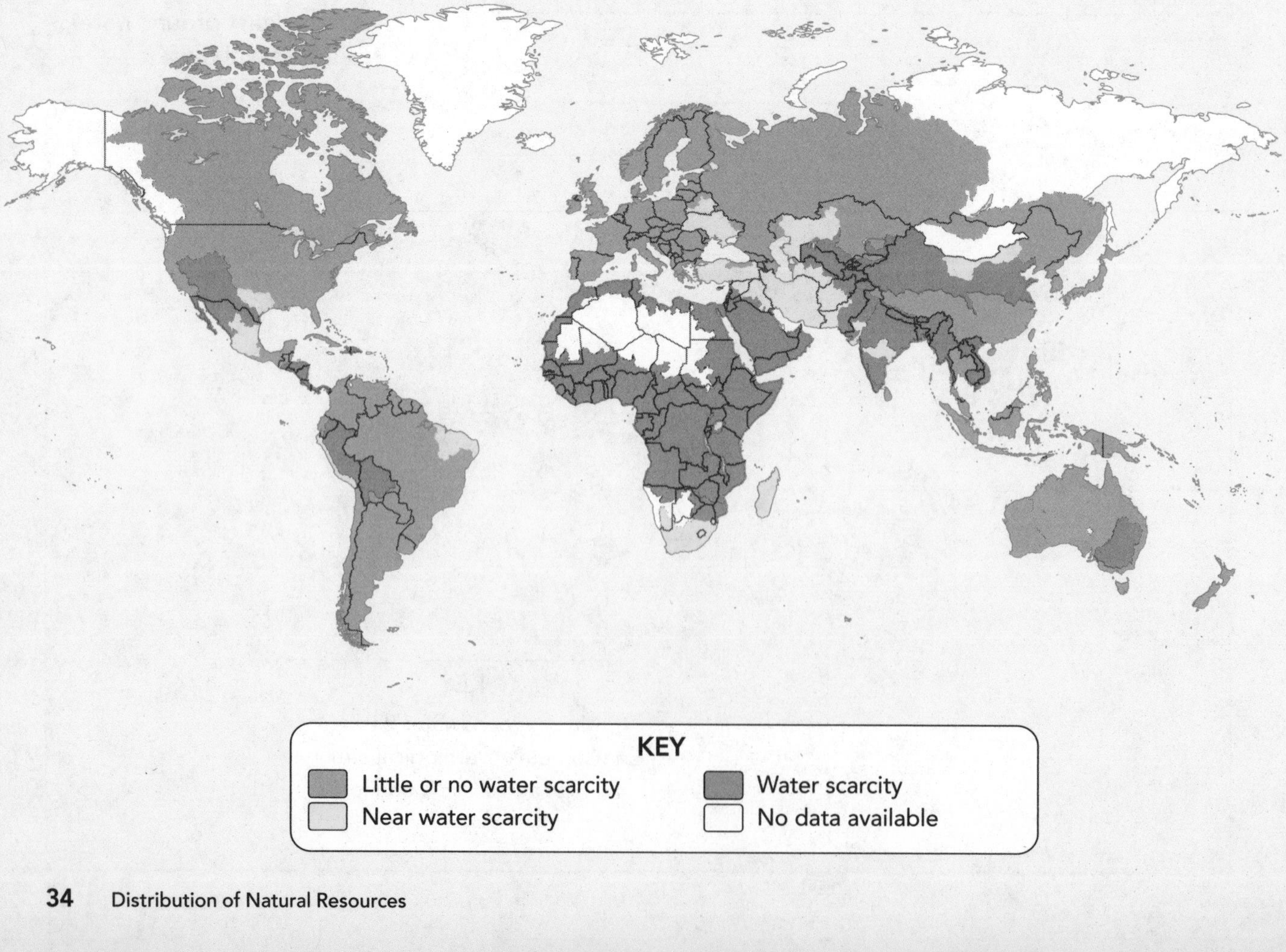
KEY
Little or no water scarcity
Near water scarcity
Water scarcity
No data available

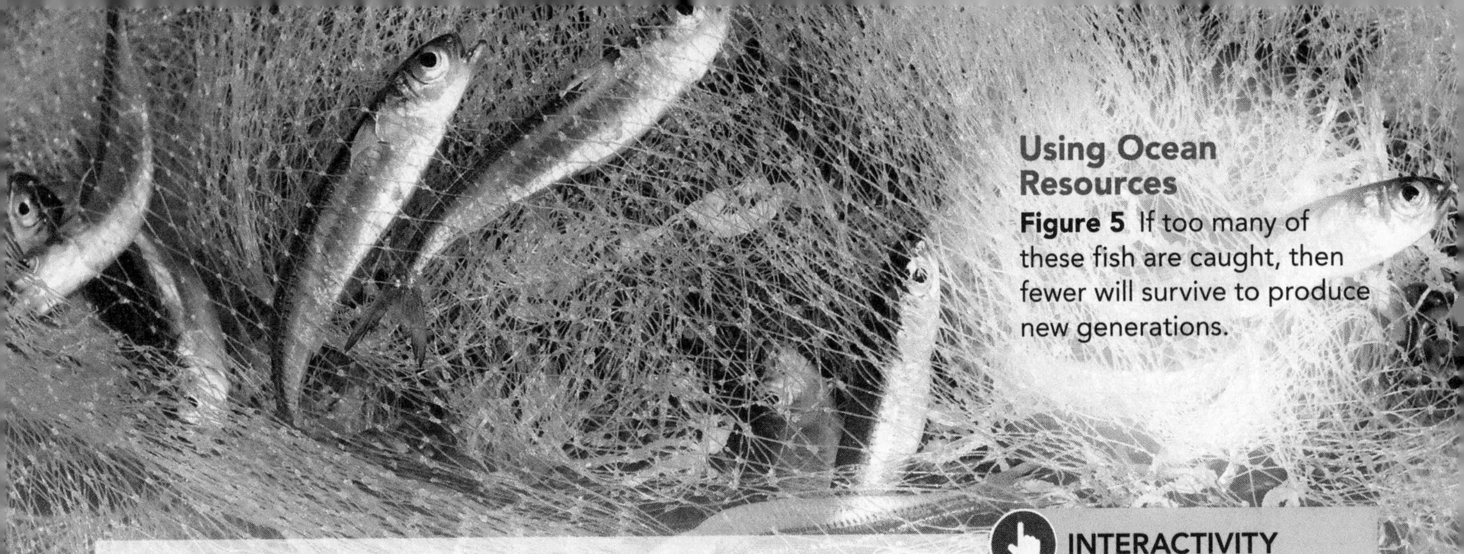

**Figure 5** If too many of these fish are caught, then fewer will survive to produce new generations.

**Desalination** In the future, humans may look to technology and the ocean to meet their water needs. The process of desalination removes salt and minerals from saltwater to make fresh water. Today, **desalination** plants around the world are costly and require a lot of energy to distill saltwater. We may eventually use solar energy to convert ocean water into fresh water.

## Other Water Resources
Humans rely on the ocean to provide a number of other important resources besides water, such as sea organisms for food and other products **(Figure 5)**. The ocean also provides salt, minerals, and fuels.

Living resources such as fish are replenished through natural cycles. However, overfishing can result in severe reductions or collapses of ocean ecosystems and the resources they provide. In addition, pollution and global climate change can have serious impacts on the biosphere resources we rely on from the ocean as well as freshwater ecosystems.

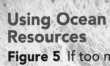

**INTERACTIVITY**

Examine the factors that affect water availability on Earth.

**CHECK POINT**

**Identify** What are some other ocean resources humans use besides water?

..................................................
..................................................
..................................................
..................................................
..................................................
..................................................

## Design It!

### Sustainable Fishing
Fish populations are replenished only if sufficient numbers are allowed to live and reproduce in their ecosystems.

**SEP Design Solutions**
Develop a design for a sustainable fishing net. Your net should function to allow only some fish to be caught, leaving others to replenish populations each year. Sketch your design in the space provided and label your sketch to explain how the net allows for sustainable fishing.

# ☑ LESSON 3 Check

**1. Identify** What are the different sources of fresh water on Earth?

....................................................................

....................................................................

....................................................................

....................................................................

....................................................................

....................................................................

**2. SEP Construct Explanations** What factors account for the uneven distribution of groundwater on Earth?

....................................................................

....................................................................

....................................................................

....................................................................

....................................................................

....................................................................

....................................................................

**3. Infer** How could the release of human waste above an aquifer affect the health of that population?

....................................................................

....................................................................

....................................................................

....................................................................

....................................................................

....................................................................

....................................................................

**4. CCC Cause and Effect** Explain why some regions are more extremely affected by water scarcity than others.

....................................................................

....................................................................

....................................................................

....................................................................

....................................................................

....................................................................

....................................................................

....................................................................

....................................................................

....................................................................

....................................................................

**5. Connect to Society** In what way does water scarcity harm the economic development of an area?

....................................................................

....................................................................

....................................................................

....................................................................

....................................................................

....................................................................

....................................................................

....................................................................

....................................................................

# Managing California's
# Water Resources

The following excerpt is from the beginning of the Sustainable Groundwater Management Act, passed by the California legislature and signed by the governor in 2014.

*(a) The Legislature finds and declares as follows:*

*(1) The people of the state have a primary interest in the protection, management, and reasonable beneficial use of the water resources of the state, both surface and underground, and that the integrated management of the state's water resources is essential to meeting its water management goals.*

*(2) Groundwater provides a significant portion of California's water supply. Groundwater accounts for more than one-third of the water used by Californians in an average year and more than one-half of the water used by Californians in a drought year when other sources are unavailable.*

*(3) Excessive groundwater extraction can cause overdraft, failed wells, deteriorated water quality, environmental damage, and irreversible land subsidence that damages infrastructure and diminishes the capacity of aquifers to store water for the future.*

*(4) When properly managed, groundwater resources will help protect communities, farms, and the environment against prolonged dry periods and climate change, preserving water supplies for existing and potential beneficial use.*

*(5) Failure to manage groundwater to prevent long-term overdraft infringes on groundwater rights.*

*(6) Groundwater resources are most effectively managed at the local or regional level.*

## CONNECT TO YOU

Find out more about California's water supply and the Sustainable Groundwater Management Act. As you research, consider these questions: How much water do Californians use? What are the sources for the state's water supply? What is the state doing to ensure that Californians have access to clean, safe water?

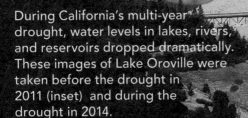

During California's multi-year drought, water levels in lakes, rivers, and reservoirs dropped dramatically. These images of Lake Oroville were taken before the drought in 2011 (inset) and during the drought in 2014.

MS-ESS3-1

## Evidence-Based Assessment

Van is researching information about the mineral copper and its distribution on Earth. Copper is used in electrical systems and even found in very small amounts in living things. Here is some of the other information Van finds, along with two maps that he finds during his research:

- copper ore can form from different geological processes

- one type of copper, called porphyry copper, is found in large deposits in certain types of rock

- most porphyry copper deposits are 340 million years old or younger

- porphyry copper forms at relatively shallow depths of about 4,500 to 9,000 meters (15,000 to 30,000 feet) in Earth's crust

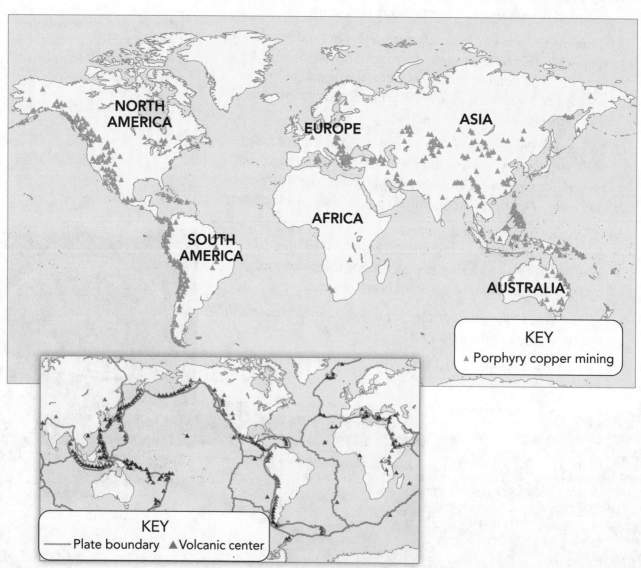

KEY
▲ Porphyry copper mining

KEY
——— Plate boundary    ▲ Volcanic center

1. **SEP Analyze Data** Which of these regions seems to have the greatest concentration of porphyry copper mining?
   **A.** Africa          **B.** Australia
   **C.** Europe          **D.** South America

2. **CCC Cause and Effect** Why are there so many volcanoes around the Pacific Ocean? Select the correct answers to complete the following sentences.

   Most volcanic activity occurs along ................. .
   **A.** faults
   **B.** plate boundaries
   **C.** mountains

   This usually happens when ................. .
   **A.** two plates meet and one slides under the other
   **B.** two plates meet and crash into each other
   **C.** two continents meet underwater

3. **CCC Patterns** Based on the map of porphyry copper mining, which of the following statements about the distribution of copper is correct? Select all that apply.

   ☐ Porphyry copper is distributed relatively evenly across most of the continents.

   ☐ Very little porphyry copper is found in Africa.

   ☐ A concentration of porphyry copper runs from Europe eastward through Asia and then south into Australia.

   ☐ Porphyry copper is widely distributed across South America.

   ☐ A majority of porphyry copper is found on continents that border the Pacific Ocean.

   ☐ There are fewer sources of porphyry copper in North America than in Asia.

4. **SEP Construct Explanations** Use evidence from the maps to explain why porphyry copper is generally found near areas where volcanic activity, often associated with plate collisions, has occurred in the past.

   .......................................................................

   .......................................................................

   .......................................................................

   .......................................................................

   .......................................................................

   .......................................................................

   .......................................................................

   .......................................................................

   .......................................................................

   .......................................................................

   .......................................................................

   .......................................................................

   .......................................................................

   .......................................................................

   .......................................................................

   .......................................................................

   .......................................................................

   .......................................................................

MS-ESS3-1

# To Drill or Not to Drill

How can you **use a model** to confirm the location of a **petroleum** deposit?

## Background

**Phenomenon**  An energy company wants to drill for oil on the outskirts of a small town. The owners of the energy company have provided evidence that the town is located near an area that was a large sea millions of years ago. Based on that evidence, they believe there is a large deposit of petroleum under the town. Town officials have hired you as an expert to look for evidence of oil under the town.

In this investigation, you will develop a model that you can use to predict whether or not the company will locate any oil below the town.

### Materials

(per group)

- aquarium gravel
- glass baking dish
- wax crayons or candles
- plastic knife
- small weight or heavy book
- hot plate

### Safety

Be sure to follow all safety guidelines provided by your teacher. The Safety Appendix of your textbook provides more details about the safety icons.

## Develop Your Model

1. Using the available materials, your group must develop a model that meets the following criteria:

   - It must show how oil forms from ancient marine organisms.

   - It must demonstrate the geological forces involved in the formation of oil.

   - It must indicate whether or not oil can form below the town.

2. Work with your group to develop ideas for a model that meets the criteria. Consider the following questions as you develop and design your model:

   - What materials can you use to represent the buried organic material that eventually forms oil?

   - How can your model demonstrate the geological forces that form oil?

   - What observations will you make?

3. After agreeing on a plan, write out the steps that your group will follow to develop and use the model. Include a sketch of the model that labels the materials you will be using and what they represent.

4. After getting your teacher's approval, construct your model and use it to demonstrate how oil forms. Record your observations and data in the space provided.

## Plan and Sketch

## Observations

# Analyze and Interpret Data

1. **SEP Use Models** Use your model to explain why oil is a nonrenewable resource.

   ...................................................................................................................

   ...................................................................................................................

   ...................................................................................................................

   ...................................................................................................................

2. **CCC Cause and Effect** What geological forces are involved in the formation of oil? How did you incorporate these forces into your model?

   ...................................................................................................................

   ...................................................................................................................

   ...................................................................................................................

   ...................................................................................................................

   ...................................................................................................................

3. **SEP Construct Explanations** Explain whether or not oil will be found under the town. Use evidence from your model to support your explanation.

   ...................................................................................................................

   ...................................................................................................................

   ...................................................................................................................

   ...................................................................................................................

   ...................................................................................................................

   ...................................................................................................................

4. **Identify Limitations** In what ways is your model not reflective of the actual conditions that lead to the formation of oil? How could your group improve the model?

   ...................................................................................................................

   ...................................................................................................................

   ...................................................................................................................

   ...................................................................................................................

   ...................................................................................................................

   ...................................................................................................................

# Ecosystems

## Investigative Phenomenon
How can you model how matter and energy cycle through an ecosystem?

**MS-LS2-1** Analyze and interpret data to provide evidence for the effects of resource availability on organisms and populations of organisms in an ecosystem.

**MS-LS2-3** Develop a model to describe the cycling of matter and flow of energy among living and nonliving parts of an ecosystem.

**EP&CIIb** Students should be developing an understanding that direct and indirect changes to natural systems due to the growth of human populations and their consumption rates influence the geographic extent, composition, biological diversity, and viability of natural systems.

**EP&CIIIa** Students should be developing an understanding that natural systems proceed through cycles and processes that are required for their functioning.

HOW are these manatees well suited to their environment?

## HANDS-ON LAB

μ**Connect** Explore how you are part of a cycle on Earth.

What questions do you have about the phenomenon?

.......................................................................................................................................

.......................................................................................................................................

.......................................................................................................................................

.......................................................................................................................................

.......................................................................................................................................

.......................................................................................................................................

.......................................................................................................................................

.......................................................................................................................................

.......................................................................................................................................

.......................................................................................................................................

.......................................................................................................................................

.......................................................................................................................................

# Quest PBL

## What do you think is causing Pleasant Pond to turn green?

**Figure It Out** In 2016, algal blooms turned bodies of water green and slimy in California, Florida, Utah, and many other states. These blooms put people and ecosystems in danger. Scientists that study lakes and other inland bodies of water, known as limnologists, are working to predict and prevent future algal blooms. In this problem-based Quest activity, you will investigate an algal bloom at a lake and determine its cause. In labs and digital activities, you will apply what you learn in each lesson to help you gather evidence to solve the mystery. With enough evidence, you will be able to identify what you believe is the cause of the algal bloom and present a solution in the Findings activity.

 **INTERACTIVITY**

Mystery at Pleasant Pond

 MS-LS2-1, MS-LS2-3, EP&CIIb, EP&CIIIa

### 🐝 NBC LEARN ▶ VIDEO

After watching the above Quest Kickoff Video, which explores the effects of a toxic algal bloom in Lake Erie, think about the impact that shutting down the water supply might have on your community. Record your ideas below.

........................................................

........................................................

........................................................

........................................................

........................................................

........................................................

........................................................

........................................................

........................................................

........................................................

# Quest CHECK-IN

## IN LESSON 1

What are some possible causes of the algal bloom in the pond? Evaluate data to identify possible explanations for the problems at the pond.

 **INTERACTIVITY**

Suspicious Activities

# Quest CHECK-IN

## IN LESSON 2

How do nutrients affect organisms in an aquatic environment? Investigate how the nonliving factors can affect the organisms in a pond.

 **INTERACTIVITY**

Nutrients and Aquatic Organisms

An algal bloom can seriously disrupt an ecosystem by interfering with an organism's ability to find food or function properly.

## Quest CHECK-IN

### IN LESSON 3

How are cycles of matter and energy affected by environmental change? Explore the cycling of matter and the flow of energy among organisms in a pond.

👆 **INTERACTIVITY**

Matter and Energy in a Pond

## Quest FINDINGS

## Complete the Quest!

Write a news story explaining what you think is the cause of the algal bloom in the pond. Tell how it has impacted the ecosystem and include a proposal for restoring the pond.

👆 **INTERACTIVITY**

Reflections on a Pond

# ① Living Things and the Environment

## HANDS-ON LAB

**ⓤInvestigate** Model how space can be a limiting factor.

**MS-LS2-1** Analyze and interpret data to provide evidence for the effects of resource availability on organisms and populations of organisms in an ecosystem. (Also **EP&CIIb**)

## Connect It !

✏ **Circle and label some of the nonliving things at the beach.**

**SEP Construct Explanations** Why are these things considered nonliving, and why do organisms need them?

...................................................................................................................................

...................................................................................................................................

...................................................................................................................................

# Organisms and Habitats

At the beach shown in **Figure 1**, animals such as California sea lions stop to molt, breed, and give birth. A sea lion is an **organism**, or living thing. Different types of organisms live in different types of surroundings, or environments. All organisms are dependent on their environmental interactions with both living things and nonliving factors. An organism interacts with its environment to get the **resources**—food, water, shelter, and other things—that it needs to live, grow, and reproduce. An environment that provides the things a specific organism needs to live, grow, and reproduce is called a **habitat**.

In nature, every organism you see in a particular habitat is there because that habitat meets the organism's needs. Some organisms have the ability to move from one habitat to another as conditions change or as different needs arise, but many organisms stay in the same habitat for their entire lives. The living and nonliving things in a particular environment and the interactions among them define the habitat and its conditions.

## HANDS-ON LAB

Explore the relationships among living and nonliving things in a local area.

## Academic Vocabulary

Have you heard the term *resources* in other contexts? List some examples.

........................................................

........................................................

........................................................

........................................................

## A Hangout in the Habitat
**Figure 1** In any environment, like La Jolla Beach located north of San Diego in California, living and nonliving things interact with each other.

INTERACTIVITY

Explore the factors in a habitat.

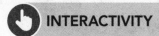

VIDEO

Explore biotic and abiotic factors in everyday life.

**Reflect** What are some of the biotic and abiotic factors in the ecosystem in which you live?

**Biotic Factors** What types of living things are in the Pacific Gopher snake's forest habitat below (**Figure 2**)? The parts of a habitat that are or were once alive and that interact with an organism are called **biotic factors**. These biological components include the trees and plants. Animals that the gopher snake eats are biotic factors, as are the other snakes it encounters. Waste products made by these organisms and others are also considered biotic factors. Bacteria, mushrooms, and other small organisms are other types of biotic factors that play important roles in the habitat.

**Abiotic Factors** Organisms also interact with nonliving things in the environment. **Abiotic factors** are the nonliving parts of an organism's habitat. These physical components include water, oxygen, space, rocks, light, temperature, and soil. The quality and condition of the abiotic factors can have a major effect on living things. For example, water in a habitat may contain pollutants. The poor quality of the water may result in sickness or death for the organisms that live there.

CHECK POINT **Cite Textual Evidence** Why do you think snakes do not live in the Arctic tundra? Use evidence from the text to support your answer.

.......................................................................

.......................................................................

**Gopher Snake Habitat**

**Figure 2** This Pacific gopher snake, native to California, interacts with many biotic and abiotic factors in its habitat.

## Design It!

**There are different biotic and abiotic factors in a habitat.**

**SEP Develop Models** Using common materials to model biotic and abiotic factors, draw a model of a local habitat. Include a key to identify what the different materials represent.

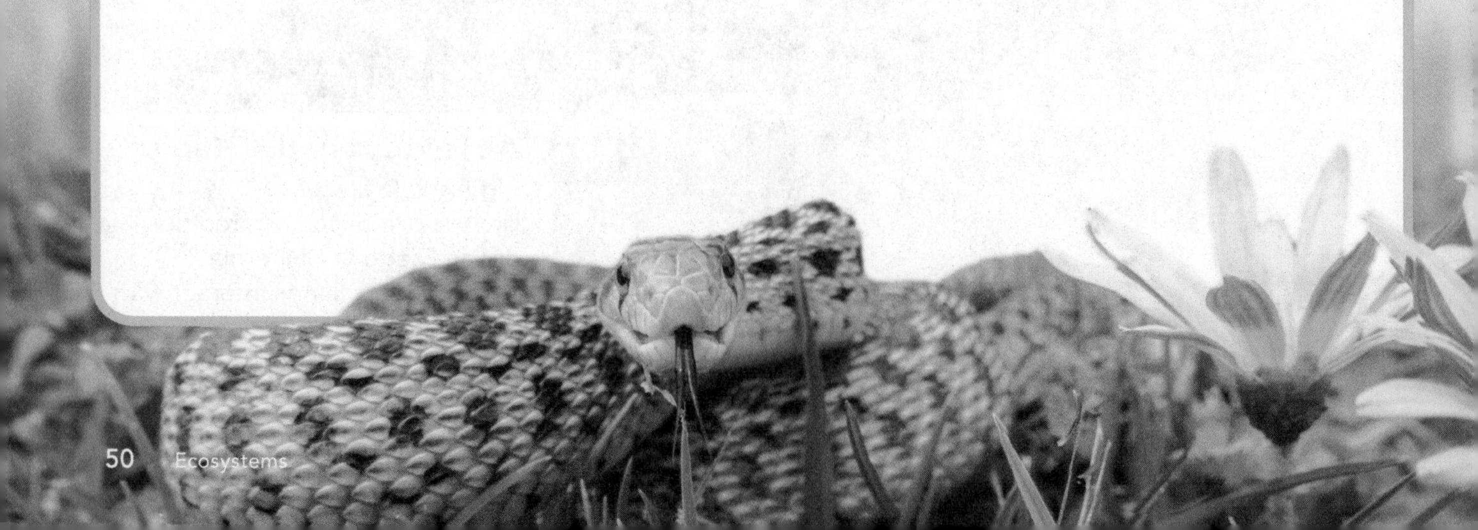

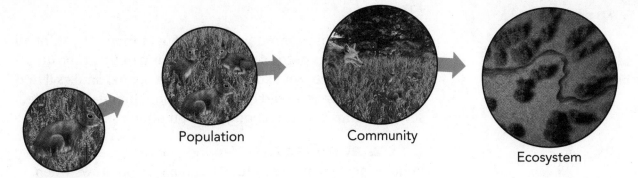

Organism

Population

Community

Ecosystem

# Ecosystem Organization

An organism rarely lives alone in its habitat. Instead, organisms live together in populations and communities that interact with abiotic factors in their ecosystems. Interactions can also occur among the various populations. **Figure 3** summarizes the levels of organization in an ecosystem.

## Organisms
All of the Sandhill cranes that live in Central California are members of one species. A species (SPEE sheez) is a group of organisms that can mate with each other and produce offspring that can also mate and reproduce.

## Populations
All the members of one species living in a particular area are referred to as a **population**. The Sandhill cranes that live in the San Joaquin Valley, for example, are one example of a population.

## Communities
A particular area usually contains more than one species of organism. The San Joaquin Valley is home to hundreds of bird species, as well as mammals, plants, and other varieties of organisms. All the different populations that live together in an area make up a **community**.

The community of organisms that lives in a particular area, along with the nonliving environment, make up an **ecosystem**. The study of how organisms interact with each other and with their environment is called ecology.

☑ CHECK POINT **Determine Meaning** What makes up a community in an ecosystem?

..............................................................................................

..............................................................................................

..............................................................................................

## Levels of Organization
**Figure 3** A single individual in an ecosystem is the organism, which forms a population with other members of its species. Different species form communities in a single ecosystem.

**CCC Systems** Make a prediction about how a lack of resources in an ecosystem might impact the levels of organization.

..........................................................

..........................................................

..........................................................

..........................................................

..........................................................

..........................................................

..........................................................

..........................................................

## Literacy Connection

**Cite Textual Evidence** Suppose farmers in an area spray insecticides on their crops. A population of birds that feeds on insects begins to decline. Underline the text that supports the idea that the insecticide may be responsible for the decline in the bird population.

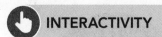

# Populations

Remember from your reading that a population consists of all of the organisms of the same species living in the same area at the same time. For example, all of the gopher snakes living in the same forest would be a distinct population. There are several things that can change a population's size.

**Births and Deaths** New individuals generally join a population by being born into it. A population grows when more individuals are born into it than die in any period of time. So when the birth rate (the number of births per 1,000 individuals for a given time period) is greater than the death rate (the number of deaths per 1,000 individuals for a given time period) a population may increase. When the birth rate is the same as the death rate, then the population usually remains stable. In situations where the death rate is greater than the birth rate, the population will decrease.

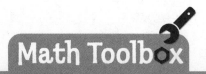

# Math Toolbox

## Graphing Population Changes

Changes over time in a population, such as deer in California, can be displayed in a graph.

### Deer Population Trends, 2000–2010

| Year | Population (estimated) | Year | Population (estimated) |
|------|------------------------|------|------------------------|
| 2000 | 509,000 | 2006 | 420,140 |
| 2001 | 674,500 | 2007 | 438,140 |
| 2002 | 554,000 | 2008 | 487,000 |
| 2003 | 525,230 | 2009 | 484,400 |
| 2004 | 475,800 | 2010 | 445,446 |
| 2005 | 602,650 | | |

**1. Represent Relationship** ✏ Use the data table to complete a graph of the changes in the deer population. Then describe the trend in the graph.

........................................................................

........................................................................

........................................................................

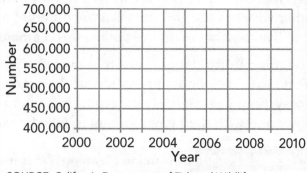

SOURCE: California Department of Fish and Wildlife

**2. SEP Interpret Data** What factors do you think might be responsible for spikes and drops in the deer population?

........................................................................

........................................................................

**Immigration and Emigration** A population's size also can increase or decrease when individuals move into or out of the population. Immigration (im ih GRAY shun) means moving into a population. Emigration (em ih GRAY shun) means leaving a population. For instance, if food is scarce, some members of the antelope herd in **Figure 4** may wander off in search of a better habitat. If they become permanently separated from the original herd, they will no longer be part of that population.

## Population Density

If you are a scientist studying an ecosystem or population, it can be helpful to know the population **density** —the number of individuals in an area of a specific size. Population density can be represented as an equation:

$$Population\ density = \frac{Number\ of\ individuals}{Unit\ area}$$

For example, suppose an ecologist estimates there are 800 beetles living in a park measuring 400 square meters. The population density would be 800 beetles per 400 square meters, or 2 beetles per square meter.

✅ CHECK POINT **Summarize Text** How do birth and death rates affect a population's size?

..................................................................................

..................................................................................

..................................................................................

HANDS-ON LAB

u**Investigate** Model how space can be a limiting factor.

**Academic Vocabulary**

Have you heard the term *density* before? What did it mean in that other context?

..................................................................

..................................................................

**Emigration**

**Figure 4** Food scarcity is just one cause of emigration.
**SEP Construct Explanations** What factors might cause individuals in this antelope herd to emigrate?

..................................................................

..................................................................

..................................................................

..................................................................

..................................................................

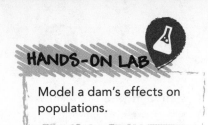
# Factors That Limit Population Growth

In any ecosystem, organisms and populations with similar requirements for food, water, oxygen, or other resources may compete with each other for limited resources. Less access to these resources consequently constrains their growth and reproduction. An environmental factor that causes a population to stop growing or to decrease in size, such as a fatal disease infecting organisms, is a **limiting factor**.

**Food and Water** Food and water can be limiting factors for virtually any population. An adult elephant eats an average of around 180 kilograms of vegetation each day to survive. Suppose the trees in its habitat can provide 1000 kilograms of vegetation daily. In this habitat, not more than 5 adult elephants could survive. The largest population that an area can support is called its carrying capacity.

**Climate and Weather** Changes in climate can limit population growth. Warmer weather in the early winter, for example, can cause some plants to continue growing. Natural disasters such as hurricanes and floods can have immediate and long-term effects on populations.

**Space and Shelter** Other limiting factors for populations are space and shelter, as illustrated by the nesting site in **Figure 5**. When individual organisms must compete for space to live or raise young, the population can decrease. Competition for suitable shelter also can limit the growth of a population.

✓ CHECK POINT **Summarize Text** How do limiting factors affect a population of organisms?

..............................................................................................

..............................................................................................

### Limited Space

**Figure 5** ✏️ In the image of the gannets, circle the available space in the environment for nesting and raising young.

**CCC Cause and Effect** How does the lack of space act as a limiting factor for these gannets?

..........................................................

..........................................................

..........................................................

..........................................................

..........................................................

# ☑ LESSON 1 Check

MS-LS2-1, EP&CIIb

**1. CCC Systems** Identify the levels of organization in an ecosystem from smallest to largest.

...................................................................

...................................................................

**Use the graph to answer questions 2 and 3.**

**Changes in Mouse Population**

**2. SEP Analyze Data** What trends do you observe in the mouse population for the four years?

...................................................................

...................................................................

...................................................................

**3. SEP Interpret Data** Does the data support the idea that this population is relatively stable? Give evidence to support your answer.

...................................................................

...................................................................

...................................................................

**4. SEP Construct Explanations** How can biotic and abiotic factors in an ecosystem affect populations? Give two examples of each.

...................................................................

...................................................................

...................................................................

...................................................................

...................................................................

...................................................................

...................................................................

**5. CCC Stability and Change** Why is climate considered to be a limiting factor for populations in an ecosystem?

...................................................................

...................................................................

...................................................................

# Quest CHECK-IN

**In this lesson, you learned how ecosystems are organized and how different factors affect populations.**

**CCC Cause and Effect** What effect might an algal bloom in a pond have on populations of organisms that make their home there?

...................................................................

...................................................................

...................................................................

...................................................................

...................................................................

...................................................................

👆 **INTERACTIVITY**

Suspicious Activities

**Go online** to research and explore explanations for the algal bloom. Then, using the information you have gathered, identify three possible causes for the bloom.

# LESSON

## 2

# Energy Flow in Ecosystems

## HANDS-ON LAB

**uInvestigate** Observe how decomposers get energy.

 **MS-LS2-3** Develop a model to describe the cycling of matter and flow of energy among living and nonliving parts of an ecosystem. (Also **EP&CIIIa**)

## Connect It!

✏️ **Shade in one of the arrows to indicate the direction in which energy flows between the tule elk and the grass.**

**CCC Energy and Matter** Where do you think the plants in the image get the energy they need to grow and survive?

.......................................................................................................

.......................................................................................................

.......................................................................................................

# Energy Roles in an Ecosystem

In gym class, have you ever been assigned to play a position like catcher or goalie for your class team? If so, you know what it's like to have a specific **role** in a system. Similar to positions in sports, every organism has a role in the movement of energy through its ecosystem.

Energy roles are based on the way organisms obtain food and interact with other organisms. In an ecosystem, organisms play the energy role of either a producer, consumer, or decomposer.

## Producers

Energy enters most ecosystems as sunlight. Some organisms, such as the terrestrial plants shown in **Figure 1** and some types of bacteria, use nonliving parts of the ecosystem to carry out life functions. For example, in a process called photosynthesis, these organisms use the sun's energy to recombine atoms from various elements and molecules of water and carbon dioxide into food molecules—all of which are nonliving.

An organism that can make its own food is a **producer**. Producers interact with the ecosystem when they become the source of food for other organisms. In terrestrial ecosystems, plants grow on the land and capture energy from sunlight. However, in an aquatic environment of the dark deep ocean, some bacteria convert chemical energy into food from hydrothermal vents in the ocean floor. They are the producers in these ecosystems that include worms, clams, and crabs.

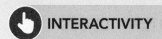

**INTERACTIVITY**

Identify the sources of your dinner.

**Academic Vocabulary**

Have you heard the term *role* in other contexts? List some examples.

........................................................

........................................................

........................................................

**Obtaining Energy**

**Figure 1** Tule elk are found only in the marshy areas and the grasslands of California's Central Valley. Their lush habitat provides them with their food of choice—tule sedge, a flowering plant that resembles grass.

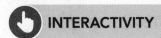

**INTERACTIVITY**

Model energy roles and energy flow in ecosystems.

**INTERACTIVITY**

Explore the roles living things play in ecosystems.

📓 **Write About It** What are some producers, consumers, scavengers, and decomposers you have seen in your neighborhood? Record your observations.

## Life and Death in an Alaskan Stream

**Figure 2** Salmon migrate upstream to this forest environment after spending most of their lives at sea. As they travel, many of them become food for the ecosystem's carnivores.

**SEP Develop Models** ✏️ Label the producers, consumers, decomposers, and scavengers in the image.

**Consumers** Organisms like the animals in **Figure 2** cannot produce their own food. Instead, one way these organisms interact with their ecosystem is by eating other organisms. A **consumer** obtains energy by feeding on other organisms.

To classify consumers according to what they eat, scientists make observations and look for patterns. As consumers eat, the food is broken down into nonliving molecules that help supply them with energy.

Consumers that eat only animals are carnivores. Great white sharks, owls, and tigers are examples of carnivores. Some carnivores are scavengers. A scavenger is a carnivore that feeds on the bodies of dead organisms. Scavengers include hagfish and condors. Some carnivores will scavenge if they cannot find live animals to prey upon.

Herbivores are consumers that eat only plants and other photosynthetic organisms. Grasshoppers, rabbits, and cows are herbivores.

Consumers that can eat both plants and animals are omnivores. Raccoons, pigs, and humans are omnivores.

**Decomposers** If the only roles in an ecosystem were producer and consumer, then some of the nonliving matter that is essential for life, such as carbon and nitrogen, would remain in the waste products and remains of dead organisms. However, decomposers have a role in ecosystems to prevent this from happening. **Decomposers** break down biotic wastes and dead organisms, returning the raw materials to the ecosystem. For example, after adult salmon swim upstream and reproduce, they die. Their carcasses litter the riverbeds and banks. Bacteria in the soil help break down the carcasses, releasing their nutrients to trees, grasses, shrubs, and other producers that depend on them.

In a sense, decomposers interact with their environment as nature's recyclers. While obtaining energy, decomposers also return nonliving matter in the form of simple molecules to the environment. These molecules can be used again by other organisms. Mushrooms, bacteria, and mold are common decomposers.

HANDS-ON LAB

✐ **Investigate** Observe how decomposers get energy.

✓ CHECK POINT **Integrate with Visuals** In terms of their energy roles, what similarities do the bear, salmon, and coyote in **Figure 2** share?

..............................................................................................

..............................................................................................

59

## Food chain

Grizzly bear

Salmon

Crustaceans

Zooplankton

Phytoplankton

# Energy and Matter Transfer

Energy in most ecosystems comes from sunlight, and producers convert this energy into food through photosynthesis. The transfer of energy can be tracked as energy flows through a natural system. The energy and matter are contained in atoms and molecules that are transferred to herbivores that eat the producers. Then they move on to carnivores feeding on the first, or primary, consumers. The energy and matter next move on through other meat-eating secondary consumers. This pattern of energy and matter movement can be described through different models: food chains, food webs, and energy pyramids.

**Food Chains**  A food chain is one way to show how energy and matter move through an ecosystem. A **food chain** is a series of events in which one organism eats another and obtains energy and nutrients. **Figure 3** illustrates one example of a food chain. The arrows indicate the movement of energy and matter as organisms are consumed up the food chain.

**Food Webs**  Energy and matter move in one direction through a food chain, but they can also take different paths through the ecosystem. However, most producers and consumers are part of many overlapping food chains. A more realistic way to show how energy and matter cycle through an ecosystem is with a food web. As shown in **Figure 4**, a **food web** consists of many overlapping food chains in an ecosystem.

Organisms may play more than one role in an ecosystem. Look at the red-tailed hawk in **Figure 4**. A hawk is a carnivore that eats mostly second-level consumers. However, when a hawk eats a kangaroo rat, it is a third-level consumer.

Humans also play a role on the natural cycling of food webs. We depend upon food webs for energy and financial gain. Yet, we can alter the natural system of a food web by destroying habitats and removing too much energy. When we do this, we interrupt the natural cycle needed for the food web to function.

## Food Chain

**Figure 3** The food chain tracing a path from the phytoplankton to the grizzly bear is a simple way of showing how energy and matter flow from one organism to the next in the Alaskan stream ecosystem shown in **Figure 2**.

**CCC System Models**  What are some limitations of modeling the flow of energy and matter in an ecosystem with a food chain?

..................................................................................................

..................................................................................................

# Model It !

## Food Web

**Figure 4** This food web depicts relationships among some of the organisms that live in the Mojave Desert in California.

**SEP Develop Models** ✏ Complete the food web by drawing and identifying the missing organisms listed below. Add arrows to the diagram to complete the web. Then, label the nonliving parts of the ecosystem.

| cactus | coyote | deer | rattlesnake |

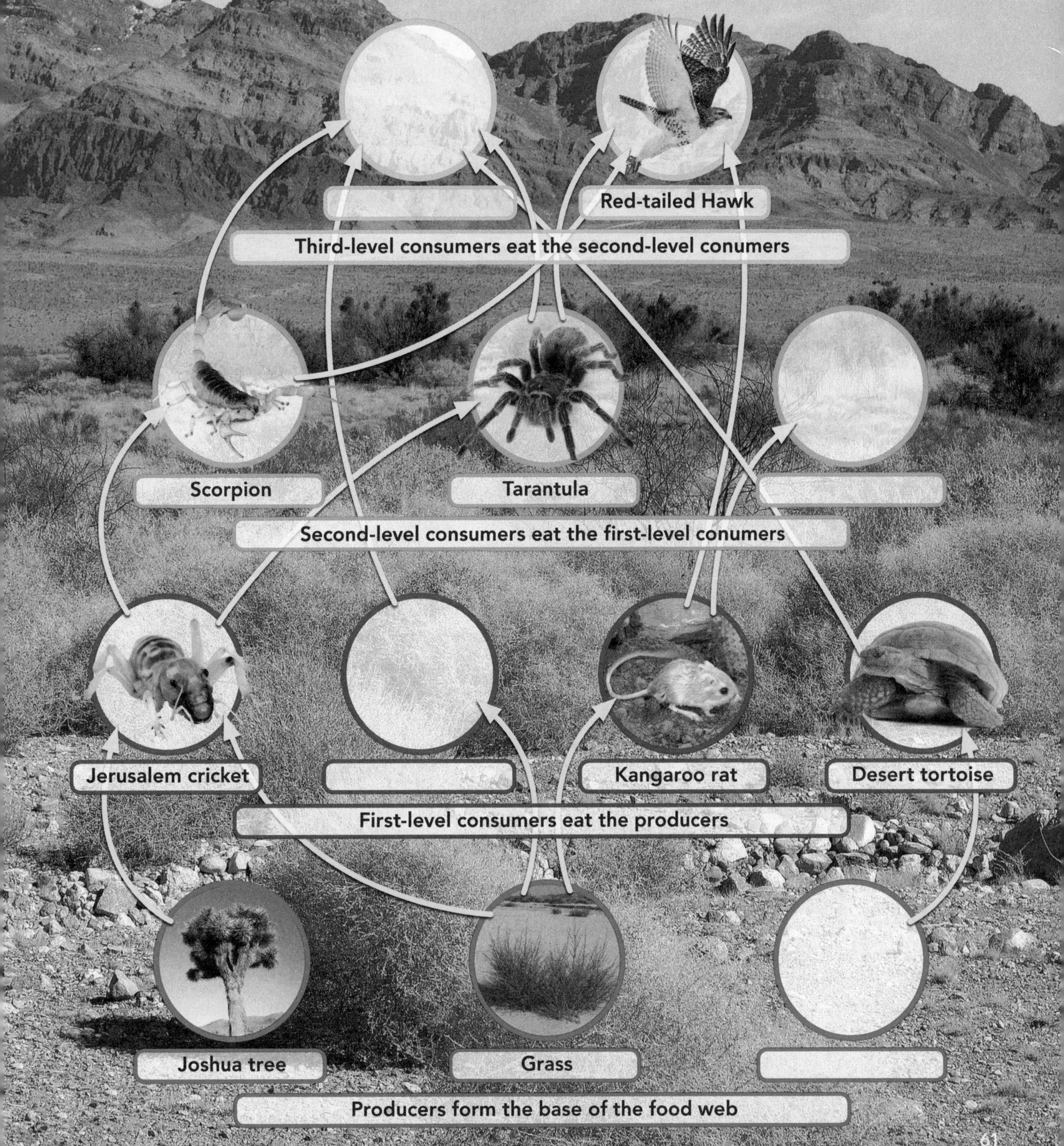

Red-tailed Hawk

**Third-level consumers eat the second-level conumers**

Scorpion          Tarantula

**Second-level consumers eat the first-level conumers**

Jerusalem cricket          Kangaroo rat          Desert tortoise

**First-level consumers eat the producers**

Joshua tree          Grass

**Producers form the base of the food web**

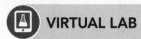

**VIRTUAL LAB**

Investigate the food web of Chesapeake Bay.

## Literacy Connection

**Integrate with Visuals**
Why is an energy pyramid shaped like a triangle with the point on top?

....................................................

....................................................

....................................................

....................................................

**Energy Pyramids** A diagram called an **energy pyramid** shows the amount of energy that moves from one feeding level to another in a food web. Each step in a food chain or food web is represented by a level within an energy pyramid, as shown in **Figure 5**. Producers have the most available energy so they make up the first level, or base, of the pyramid. Energy moves up the pyramid from the producers, to the first-level consumers, to the second-level consumers, and so on. There is no limit to the number of levels in a food web or energy pyramid. However, each level has less energy available than the level below. When more levels exist between a producer and a consumer, a smaller percentage of the producer's original energy is available to that consumer.

When an organism consumes food, it obtains energy and matter used to carry out life activities. These activities produce heat, which is released and lost to the environment, reducing the amount of energy available to the next level.

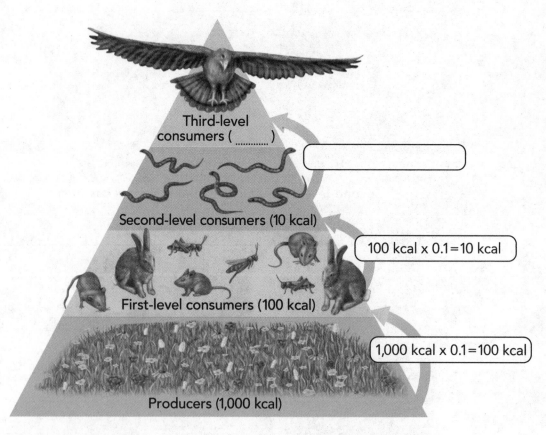

Third-level consumers ( .......... )

Second-level consumers (10 kcal)

100 kcal x 0.1=10 kcal

First-level consumers (100 kcal)

1,000 kcal x 0.1=100 kcal

Producers (1,000 kcal)

**Energy Pyramid**

**Figure 5** This energy pyramid shows how the amount of available energy decreases as you move up an energy pyramid from the producers to the different levels of consumers. Only about 10 percent of the energy is transferred from level to level. Energy is measured in kilocalories, or kcal.

**SEP Use Mathematics** ✏ Write in the missing equation and fill in the energy that gets to the hawk at the top.

## Energy Availability

As you can see in **Figure 5**, only about 10 percent of the energy at one level of a food web is available to the next higher level. This greatly limits how many different levels a food chain can have, as well as the numbers of organisms that can be supported at higher levels. This is why it is typical for there to be fewer organisms as you move from one level of a pyramid or one "link" in a food chain up to the next level.

☑ CHECK POINT **Summarize Text** Why is energy reduced at each level of the energy pyramid?

...........................................................................................................

...........................................................................................................

...........................................................................................................

🖐 **INTERACTIVITY**

Model how altering a food web affects the flow of energy and matter in an ecosystem.

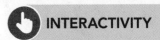

# Math Toolbox

## Relationships in an Energy Pyramid

In the San Francisco Bay Area Delta ecosystem, shrimp eat algae. Chinook salmon eat the shrimp, and great blue herons eat the Chinook salmon. Suppose that the algae contain 550,000 kilocalories.

1. SEP **Calculate** 🖊 Complete the pyramid by calculating the energy available to each level.

2. **Analyze Proportional Relationships** How would the amount of energy in the pyramid change if the shrimp ate only half of the available algae?

.........................................................................

.........................................................................

.........................................................................

.........................................................................

.........................................................................

.........................................................................

.........................................................................

Third-level consumers

Second-level consumers

First-level consumers

550,000 kcal

Producers

# ☑LESSON 2 Check

**1. CCC System Models** Which model best illustrates the flow of energy and matter in an ecosystem—a food chain or a food web? Explain.

..............................................................................
..............................................................................
..............................................................................
..............................................................................
..............................................................................

**2. SEP Evaluate Information** A student says an organism that is both a first-level and second-level consumer is an omnivore. Is that student correct? Explain.

..............................................................................
..............................................................................

**3. CCC Energy and Matter** Suppose a rancher wants to buy some grassland to raise cattle. What should she know about energy flow before she invests in the land or the cattle?

..............................................................................
..............................................................................
..............................................................................
..............................................................................
..............................................................................
..............................................................................

**4. CCC Patterns** In Massachusetts, a team of scientists studying great white sharks estimates that a population of 15,000 seals supports fewer than 100 sharks during the summer. Why are there so few top-level consumers in this system?

..............................................................................
..............................................................................
..............................................................................
..............................................................................
..............................................................................
..............................................................................

**5. SEP Construct Explanations** Human activity can affect ecosystems by removing producers, consumers, and decomposers. What limiting factors may result from human actions, and what effects might they have on the flow of energy and matter in an ecosystem?

..............................................................................
..............................................................................
..............................................................................
..............................................................................
..............................................................................
..............................................................................

# Quest CHECK-IN

**In this lesson, you learned about the general roles that organisms can play in an ecosystem, as well as how relationships among those roles can be modeled through food chains, food webs, and energy pyramids.**

**CCC Stability and Change** How might knowing about energy roles help you understand what's happening in the pond?

..............................................................................
..............................................................................

## ☞ INTERACTIVITY

Nutrients and Aquatic Organisms

**Go online** to analyze what might happen to a pond ecosystem when nutrient levels are altered. Then discuss how the results of your analysis could help you solve the mystery.

MS-LS2-1, MS-LS2-3, EP&CIIb, EP&CIIIa

# Eating Oil

**Do you know how** tiny organisms can clean up oil spills? You engineer it! Strategies used to deal with the Deepwater Horizon oil spill, the worst in U.S. history, show us how.

**The Challenge:** To clean up harmful oil from marine environments

**Phenomenon** On April 20, 2010, part of an oil rig in the Gulf of Mexico exploded. It leaked oil for 87 days. By the time the leak was fixed, about 200 million gallons of oil had spilled into the water. Oil destroys beaches, marshlands, and marine ecosystems. It coats birds, fish, and marine animals, such as dolphins and sea turtles. The oil makes it difficult for many animals to move and get food, and causes others to suffocate.

Ecologists engineered a solution that relied on nature to help with the cleanup. They poured chemicals into the water that helped break up the oil into smaller droplets. Then the bacteria and fungi in the water broke down the oil droplets.

Bioremediation uses natural living things to reduce contaminants in an environment. In the event of an oil spill, oil-eating populations of bacteria and fungi grow quickly. Now, scientists are working to engineer ways to increase the speed at which these decomposers work and to make sure the oceans can support optimal populations of these tiny oil eaters.

**INTERACTIVITY**

Design your own method to clean up an oil spill.

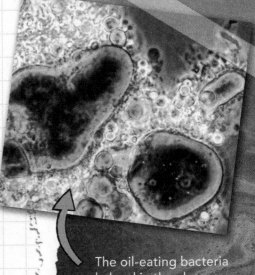

The oil-eating bacteria helped in the cleanup after the Deepwater Horizon oil spill.

## DESIGN CHALLENGE

Can you put decomposers to work and build your own composter? Go to the Engineering Design Notebook to find out!

# ③ Cycles of Matter

## HANDS-ON LAB

### uInvestigate Model the water cycle.

 **MS-LS2-3** Develop a model to describe the cycling of matter and flow of energy among living and nonliving parts of an ecosystem. (Also **EP&CIIIa**)

## Connect It !

✏️ **Draw arrows on Figure 1 and label them to show how energy enters and leaves the terrarium.**

**CCC Cause and Effect** What would happen to the ecosystem in the terrarium if it were a closed system for energy?

.................................................................................................................

.................................................................................................................

**SEP Explain Phenomena** Why is this ecosystem considered a closed system and how could that system be changed?

.................................................................................................................

.................................................................................................................

.................................................................................................................

.................................................................................................................

# Conservation of Matter and Energy

During photosynthesis and cellular respiration, matter and energy change form but the amounts stay the same. The Law of Conservation of Mass states that matter is neither created nor destroyed during any chemical or physical change. The Law of Conservation of Energy states that when one form of energy is transformed to another, no energy is lost in the process. Energy cannot be created or destroyed, but it can change from one form to another. The cycling of matter and energy can be observed in natural systems.

All over Earth, the transfer of matter and energy can be tracked as they flow through natural systems. For example, the terrarium in **Figure 1** is a closed **system** for matter. Matter cannot enter or exit. The plants, soil, air, rocks, water, microorganisms, and animals in the terrarium are all **components** of the system. As natural systems cycle, these components change form, but their total mass remains the same.

☑ CHECK POINT **Summarize Text** What would you tell a classmate who claims that food is destroyed when you eat it?

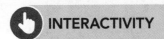
**INTERACTIVITY**

Consider your role in the cycling of energy.

**Academic Vocabulary**
The schools in one area are often called a *school system*. What are some of the *components* of this system?

........................................................

........................................................

........................................................

........................................................

**Ecosystem in a Jar**
**Figure 1** After it is sealed, a terrarium becomes a closed system for matter. But energy can still flow in and out through the glass.

## Water Cycle

Recall that matter is made up of tiny particles called atoms and two or more atoms can join to make a molecule. Two hydrogen atoms combined with one oxygen atom forms a molecule of water.

Water is essential for life. Water cycles in a continuous process from Earth's surface to the atmosphere and back. As energy is transferred through the water cycle, it can be tracked as it changes into various forms, or states. The water cycle involves the processes of evaporation, condensation, and precipitation. Follow along on **Figure 3** as you read about each process.

### Evaporation
Water molecules move from Earth's surface into the atmosphere by evaporation. **Evaporation** is the process by which molecules at the surface of liquid water absorb enough energy to change to a gas. This water vapor rises into the atmosphere as part of atmospheric convection. The energy needed for evaporation comes from sunlight. Water evaporates from oceans, lakes, fields, and other places. Smaller amounts of water also evaporate from living things. For example, plants release water vapor from their leaves. In addition, animals release liquid water in their wastes and water vapor when they exhale. You may recall that one of the products of cellular respiration is water.

**Spring Water**
**Figure 2** The water at Yellow Springs is high in iron, which stains the rocks orange.

## Model It !

**Where does your water come from?**

Yellow Springs, Ohio, shown in **Figure 2**, has been a source of refreshing water for animals and people for centuries. Geologists studying the Yellow Spring have determined that the spring is fed by rain that falls only a few miles north. After the rain soaks into the ground, it travels underground for 12 to 18 months before flowing out of the spring.

SEP Develop Models ✏ Does your drinking water come from a central water supply, a well, or bottles? Identify the source of your water and trace its origin back as far as you can. Make a model of the path the water takes to get to your home.

**Condensation** Rising water vapor reaches a point in the atmosphere where it cools. As it cools, it turns back into small droplets of water in a liquid state. The process of a gas changing to a liquid is **condensation.** The water droplets collect around dust particles and eventually form clouds. Dew is water that has condensed on plants or other objects on a cool morning.

**Precipitation** Condensing water vapor collects as clouds, but as the drops continue to grow larger, they become heavier. Eventually the heavy drops fall in the form of **precipitation:** rain, snow, sleet, or hail. Precipitation can fall into oceans, lakes, or rivers. Precipitation falling on land may soak into the soil and become groundwater, or it may run off the land and flow into rivers or oceans.

## HANDS-ON LAB

**Investigate** Model the water cycle.

**Write About It** Think how you interacted with water today. Where did that water come from? Where did it go next? Write a story that traces the water molecule's trip.

**The Water Cycle**

**Figure 3** The water you drink may have passed through the water cycle millions of times. Tomorrow, those molecules from your drink could be part of a cloud, a drop of rain, a stream, or water vapor in the air.

**CCC Systems** Label the three processes of the water cycle.

✓ CHECK POINT **Determine Central Ideas** Explain how water vapor in the air can end up as water in the ocean.

........................................................................................

........................................................................................

........................................................................................

# Carbon and Oxygen Cycles

Carbon and oxygen are essential for life. Carbon is the building block of living things. For example, carbon is a major component of bones and the proteins that build muscles. Most organisms also use oxygen for their life processes. **Figure 4** shows how carbon and oxygen cycles in ecosystems are linked. Producers, consumers, and decomposers all play roles in recycling carbon and oxygen.

**Carbon Cycle** Most producers take in carbon dioxide gas from the air during photosynthesis. Producers use the carbon to make food—carbon-containing molecules, such as sugars and starches. Carbon is also converted by plants to compounds that help plants grow. Consumers eat other organisms and take in their carbon compounds. When producers and consumers then break down the food to obtain energy, they release carbon dioxide and water into the environment. When organisms die, decomposers break down the remains, and release carbon compounds to the soil where it is available for use. Some decomposers also release carbon dioxide into the air.

**Oxygen Cycle** Oxygen also cycles through ecosystems. Producers release oxygen as a product of photosynthesis. Most organisms take in oxygen from the air or water and use it to carry out cellular respiration.

## Literacy Connection

**Determine Central Ideas** Work with a partner. Think about one food you have eaten recently. Where did the carbon in that food come from? Was the food made from plants, animals, fungi, or bacteria—or all of those sources? Where will the carbon go now that you have eaten the food? Share your response with another pair of students.

### The Carbon and Oxygen Cycles

**Figure 4** Producers, consumers, and decomposers all play roles in recycling carbon and oxygen.

**SEP Develop Models** ✏ Draw arrows to show how carbon and oxygen move through the ecosystem.

Oxygen ($O_2$) in the air

Carbon compounds in the soil

## Law of Conservation

On Earth, the atoms that make up the organisms in an ecosystem are cycled repeatedly between living and nonliving parts of the ecosystem. For example, the number of carbon and oxygen atoms remains constant when producers undergo photosynthesis. The Law of Conservation of Mass also supports that atoms may appear in different chemical compounds as they cycle through Earth's systems, but these atoms are never created or destroyed.

## Human Impact

Some human activities affect the levels of carbon and oxygen in the air. When humans burn gasoline, natural gas, and plant fuels, carbon dioxide is released into the atmosphere. Carbon dioxide levels also rise when humans clear forests to create farmland or to use the wood for fuel.

When trees are removed from an ecosystem, there are fewer producers to absorb carbon dioxide. If fallen trees are left on the ground, decomposers will break down their tissues through cellular respiration and release carbon dioxide into the air. Burning the trees has the same effect, because carbon dioxide is produced during combustion.

☑ CHECK POINT **Summarize Text** Describe the roles of producers and consumers in the oxygen cycle.

.............................................................................................................................

.............................................................................................................................

.............................................................................................................................

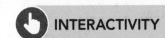

**INTERACTIVITY**

Investigate and identify the cycles of matter.

Carbon dioxide ($CO_2$) in the air

71

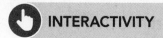
# Nitrogen Cycle in Ecosystems

Like carbon, nitrogen is one of the necessary elements of life. Nitrogen is an important component for building proteins in animals and an essential nutrient for plants. In the nitrogen cycle, nitrogen moves from the air into the soil, into living things, and back into the air or soil. The air around you is about 78 percent nitrogen gas ($N_2$). However, most organisms cannot use nitrogen gas. Nitrogen gas is called "free" nitrogen because it is not combined with other kinds of atoms.

**Nitrogen Fixation** Most organisms can use nitrogen only after it has been "fixed," or combined with other elements to form nitrogen-containing compounds. Nitrogen fixation is the process of changing free nitrogen into a usable form of nitrogen, as shown in **Figure 5**. Certain bacteria perform most nitrogen fixation. These bacteria live in bumps called nodules on the roots of legume plants. Clover, beans, peas, alfalfa, peanuts, and trees such as mesquite and desert ironwood are all common legume plants. Nitrogen can also be "fixed" by lightning. About 10 percent of the nitrogen needed by plants is fixed by lightning.

## Nitrogen Cycle

**Figure 5** In the nitrogen cycle, free nitrogen from the air is fixed into compounds. Consumers can then use these nitrogen compounds to carry out their life processes.

**CCC System Models**
✎ Circle the steps where free nitrogen is changed to a form plants and animals can use.

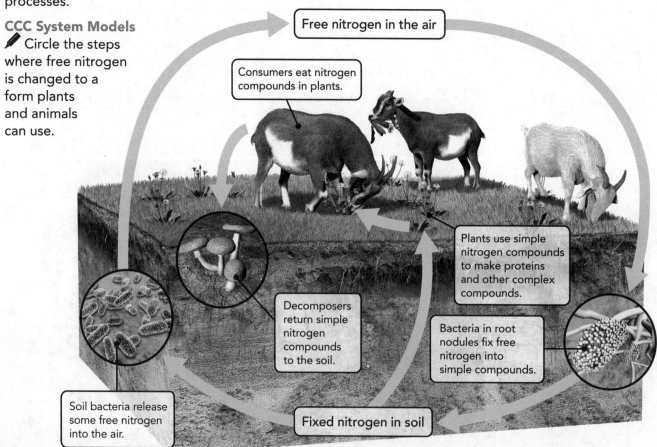

Free nitrogen in the air

Consumers eat nitrogen compounds in plants.

Plants use simple nitrogen compounds to make proteins and other complex compounds.

Decomposers return simple nitrogen compounds to the soil.

Bacteria in root nodules fix free nitrogen into simple compounds.

Soil bacteria release some free nitrogen into the air.

Fixed nitrogen in soil

**Recycling Free Nitrogen** Once nitrogen has been fixed, producers can use it to build proteins and other complex molecules. Nitrogen can cycle from the soil to producers and then to consumers many times. At some point, however, bacteria break down the nitrogen compounds into free nitrogen. The free nitrogen rises back into the air and the cycle begins again. This is also an example of the Law of Conservation of Mass. Throughout the cycling of nitrogen, the number of atoms remains constant. Nitrogen atoms may take the form of gas (free nitrogen) or they may take the form of nitrogen-containing compounds, but the atoms are never created or destroyed.

✔ CHECK POINT **Summarize Text** Why is nitrogen fixation necessary?

........................................................................................................

## Dependent and Independent Variables

Soybean plants are legumes that host nitrogen-fixing bacteria in their root nodules. Researchers wanted to know whether the plants would produce more seeds if nitrogen-fixing bacteria called *Rhizobia* were added to the soil during planting. The graph below shows the results of the experiment.

1. **Analyze Relationships**
   ✏ Underline the independent variable and circle the dependent variable in the graph. Then explain their relationship.

   ......................................................

   ......................................................

2. **CCC Use Mathematics** Write an equation that represents the difference in seed yield between beans without treatment and beans with treatment.

   ......................................................

   ......................................................

   ......................................................

   ......................................................

   ......................................................

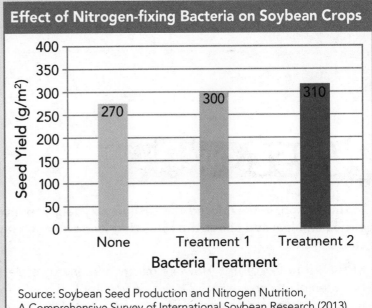

Effect of Nitrogen-fixing Bacteria on Soybean Crops

Source: Soybean Seed Production and Nitrogen Nutrition, A Comprehensive Survey of International Soybean Research (2013)

3. **SEP Interpret Data** Did the bacterial treatment have any effect? Use evidence from the graph and your equation to support your answer.

   ..............................................................................................................

   ..............................................................................................................

   ..............................................................................................................

# ☑️ LESSON 3 Check

🔗 MS-LS2-3, EP&CIIIa

**1. CCC Systems** What are the two roles of bacteria in the nitrogen cycle?

.......................................................................

.......................................................................

.......................................................................

**2. SEP Construct Explanations** How does water get up to the atmosphere, and how does it get back down to Earth's surface?

.......................................................................

.......................................................................

.......................................................................

.......................................................................

**3. SEP Develop Models** ✏️ Sketch and label a diagram showing how carbon cycles through an ecosystem.

**4. CCC Apply Concepts** How does the Law of Conservation of Mass apply to Earth's recycling of water, oxygen, carbon, and nitrogen. Give one example.

.......................................................................

.......................................................................

.......................................................................

.......................................................................

**5. CCC Energy and Matter** Compare the cycling of water and nutrients through an ecosystem to the cycling of blood in your cardiovascular system. What is the source of energy in each case?

.......................................................................

.......................................................................

.......................................................................

.......................................................................

.......................................................................

.......................................................................

.......................................................................

.......................................................................

# Quest CHECK-IN

**In this lesson, you explored the carbon, oxygen, and nitrogen cycles and learned about the roles that living things play in these cycles.**

**SEP Define Problems** How are matter and energy cycled between plants and animals? How can you apply this information to help you determine what is happening to the pond?

.......................................................................

.......................................................................

.......................................................................

.......................................................................

👆 **INTERACTIVITY**

Matter and Energy in a Pond

**Go online** to investigate how matter and energy are cycled in a pond ecosystem.

MS-LS2-1, MS-LS2-3, EP&CIVb

# An Appetite for Plastic?!

Organic materials, such as bone and leaves, get cycled through ecosystems by decomposers. Materials like rock and metal break down more slowly. Plastics, however, are manufactured products that cannot be broken down easily. Additionally, they are problematic for the environment. Scientists have been trying for decades to discover a way to degrade plastic. Now, it seems they may have found an answer inside the guts of two tiny larvae.

Wax worms live in beehives where they feed off beeswax. What is bad for bees, may be good for people who are looking for a way to deal with Earth's plastic problem. Scientists have found out that wax worms can digest plastic bags! How they do this isn't clear yet. It may be that bacteria living in the wax worm's gut allow it to break down the plastic. Another possibility is that the wax worm produces an enzyme, a substance that speeds up reactions in an organism's body, that helps it degrade the plastic.

Wax worms aren't the only ones getting attention for their eating habits! Mealworms are the larvae of a species of beetle. They are fed to pet reptiles, fish, and birds. Scientists have observed that mealworms can break down plastic foam, such as the kind used in coffee cups and packing materials.

Scientists are trying to figure out how these larvae are able to degrade plastic. It may be a long time before we figure out how to use that knowledge on a scale large enough to reduce global plastic pollution.

## MY DISCOVERY

Use the Internet or other sources to investigate how wax worms and mealworms are able to break down different types of plastics. Create a presentation that includes a visual display that shows what type of plastic each larva can eat and how its body is able to break down plastic. Then, share your presentation with the class.

Mealworms are able to break down plastic foam.

A wax worm can munch its way through through a plastic shopping bag.

MS-LS2-3

## Evidence-Based Assessment

A team of field biologists is studying energy roles and relationships among organisms in a tropical rainforest habitat in Southeast Asia. One of the biologists diagrams some of these relationships in a food web.

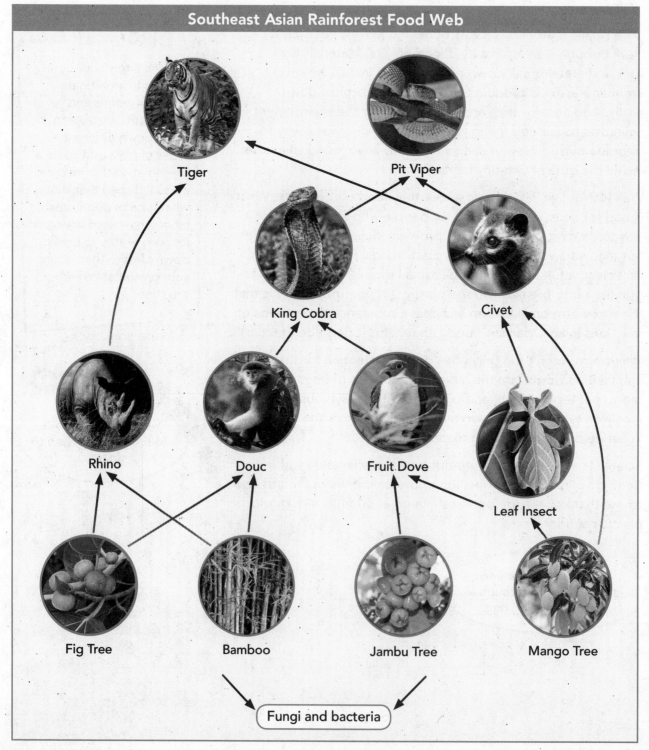

### Southeast Asian Rainforest Food Web

Tiger

Pit Viper

King Cobra

Civet

Rhino

Douc

Fruit Dove

Leaf Insect

Fig Tree

Bamboo

Jambu Tree

Mango Tree

Fungi and bacteria

1. **SEP Use Models** Which organism from the food web is a producer?

A. bamboo      B. civet

C. douc      D. tiger

2. **CCC Energy and Matter** Why are there usually fewer organisms at the top level of a food web?

........................................................................

........................................................................

........................................................................

........................................................................

........................................................................

3. **CCC System Models** What is the role of decomposers in the cycling of matter between the living and nonliving parts of the Southeast Asian rainforest ecosystem? Select all that apply.

☐ Decomposers are producers.

☐ Decomposers break down matter from dead organisms.

☐ Decomposers only interact with living parts of the ecosystem.

☐ Decomposers return biotic matter to soil, water, and air.

4. **CCC Stability and Change** If the jambu tree were removed from the food web, how would it impact the Southeast Asian rainforest ecosystem? Order the events from 1 to 4, with 1 being the first event to take place after the removal of the jambu tree and 4 being the last.

............. The douc population would decrease.

............. The king cobra population would decrease.

............. The fruit dove population would decrease.

............. The pit viper population would decrease.

5. **SEP Construct Explanations** As matter is cycled and energy flows through this system, how are both conserved? Use details from the food web to support your response.

........................................................................

........................................................................

........................................................................

........................................................................

........................................................................

........................................................................

........................................................................

........................................................................

........................................................................

........................................................................

# Quest FINDINGS

## Complete the Quest!

**Phenomenon** Identify what you believe is the cause of the algal bloom at Pleasant Pond, and describe the impact it has had on the organisms in this ecosystem. Include a proposal about restoring the pond using evidence from your investigation.

**CCC Cause and Effect** What is the connection between the water in Pleasant Pond—an abiotic factor—and the biotic factors?

........................................................................

........................................................................

........................................................................

........................................................................

**INTERACTIVITY**

Reflections on a Pond

# Last Remains

How can you **confirm** an owl's role in a **food web**?

## Background

**Phenomenon** Your neighborhood has a rodent problem! Squirrels and mice seem to be taking over. Some members of your neighborhood have suggested that introducing more barn owls into the neighborhood will bring the rodent population under control. But people want to be sure that barn owls do hunt and eat mice and squirrels before they go to the trouble of introducing these nocturnal birds to the area.

You will design and carry out an investigation by observing remains found in an owl pellet—undigested material an owl spits up. You will relate your findings to food webs and energy flow in the owl's ecosystem. Using the evidence you have collected, you will confirm whether or not the idea to introduce more barn owls into your area will help to bring the rodent population under control.

## Materials

(per group)
- goggles, 2 pair
- gloves, 2 pair
- owl pellet, 1 per group
- probes, 2
- tweezers, 1 pair
- hand lens
- paper towels
- bone identification charts

## Safety

Be sure to follow all safety guidelines provided by your teacher. The Safety Appendix of your textbook provides more details about the safety icons.

Barn owl

House mouse

Gray squirrel

## Design Your Investigation

1. Your investigation will involve observing an owl pellet, which is regurgitated or "spit up" remains of food. Owls generally eat their prey whole and then get rid of the parts of the organisms that they cannot digest, such as bones and fur.

2. Design a procedure for your investigation. Consider the following questions to help develop your plan:
   - How will you use the materials provided by your teacher?
   - What observations will you make?
   - How will you use the remains in the pellet to determine what the owl eats?
   - How can you use the bone identification charts to help you identify the remains of organisms?

3. Write the procedure for your investigation in the space provided.

4. Create a data table to record your observations. Include whether each organism you find inside the owl pellet is a herbivore, a carnivore, or an omnivore.

5.  After receiving your teacher's approval for the procedure you developed, carry out your investigation.

### HANDS-ON LAB

**uDemonstrate** Go online for a downloadable worksheet of this lab.

## Procedure

## Data Table and Observations

# Analyze and Interpret Data

1. **SEP Develop Models** Diagram the cycling of matter and energy in the barn owl's habitat. Begin by drawing a food chain. Then develop the food chain into a simple food web using additional organisms that you might find in the habitat. Include captions for your diagram that explain the cycling matter and flow of energy among the organisms.

2. **Claim** Do you think the introduction of more barn owls into your neighborhood will solve your mouse and squirrel problem? Use evidence from your investigation to support your response.

........................................................................................................

........................................................................................................

........................................................................................................

........................................................................................................

3. **Evidence** What information did you find out by observing the remains in the owl pellet?

........................................................................................................

........................................................................................................

........................................................................................................

........................................................................................................

4. **Reasoning** Owls hunt at night. Using your findings from the owl pellet, what conclusions can you draw about whether squirrels and mice are more active during the day or at night?

........................................................................................................

........................................................................................................

........................................................................................................

........................................................................................................

MS-ESS3-1, EP&CIa, EP&CIIa, EP&CIIb, EP&CIIc,
EP&CIIIa, EP&CIIIb, EP&CIIIc, EP&CIVa, EP&CIVb,
EP&CIVc, EP&CVa, EP&CVb

# Phosphorus Fiasco

**W**ithout phosphorus, living things would not exist on Earth. All animals and plants need phosphorus to produce the energy that keeps them alive and allows populations to survive. Unfortunately, like all minerals, phosphorus is not a renewable resource. Only a certain amount exists in nature, where it moves in a natural cycle. In recent years, however, that cycle has been broken, and we run the risk of using up Earth's supply of phosphorus.

In the phosphorus cycle, animals and people eat phosphorus-rich plants. The excess phosphorus leaves the bodies of organisms as waste. The waste returns to the soil to enrich the plants, starting the cycle again.

For many centuries, farmers used manure, which is rich in phosphorus, to fertilize their crops. About 175 years ago, as the population grew, farmers looked for new sources of fertilizer to keep up with the demand for food. Engineers and geologists realized that phosphorus might be mined from underground and used to manufacture fertilizers. Most of the world's phosphorus reserves are in the United States, China, Russia, and northern Africa.

The "phosphorus fiasco" is a result of improved technology that has interrupted the natural phosphorus cycle. Sewage and runoff from heavily-fertilized farmland often ends up in bodies of water where the excess phosphorus can disrupt ecosystems and result in die-offs of populations. The mining and overuse of phosphorus also poses a threat to reserves of this important element.

Phosphorus mining has altered the natural phosphorus cycle.

| World Phosphate Mine Production and Reserves | | | |
| --- | --- | --- | --- |
| Country | Mine Production (tons) | | Reserves |
| | 2015 | 2016 | |
| China | 120,000 | 138,000 | 3,100,000 |
| Jordan | 8,340 | 8,300 | 1,200,000 |
| Morocco/Western Sahara | 29,000 | 30,000 | 50,000,000 |
| Russia | 11,600 | 11,600 | 1,300,000 |
| United States | 27,400 | 27,800 | 1,100,000 |

Source: U.S. Geological Survey, 2017

**Use the text and the data table to answer the following questions.**

1. CCC Scale, Proportion, and Quantity Which country saw the greatest increase in phosphorus production between 2015 and 2016? Describe the amount of the increase as a fraction or percentage.

2. CCC Cause and Effect How have technological developments affected the natural phosphorus cycle? What do you think can be done to address this problem?

3. SEP Analyze Data Based on its current rate of production, in how many years will the United States use up its known reserves of phosphate?

4. SEP Construct Explanations Morocco/Western Sahara has by far the greatest reserves of phosphorus, but it is not the largest producer. Why do you think this is the case? Do you think the situation might change? Explain.

MS-LS2-1, EP&CIIa, EP&CIIb, EP&CIIc, EP&CIVa, EP&CIVc

THE CASE OF THE DISAPPEARING

# Cerulean Warbler

The cerulean warbler is a small, migratory songbird named for its blue color. Cerulean warblers breed in eastern North America during the spring and summer. The warblers spend the winter months in the Andes Mountains of Colombia, Venezuela, Ecuador, and Peru in the northern part of South America.

The population of cerulean warblers is decreasing very quickly. No other population of songbirds is decreasing more rapidly in eastern North America. Populations of warblers have been declining at a rate of about 3 percent a year. This means that there are 3 percent fewer warblers from one year to the next. Habitat loss, especially in the region where the birds spend the winter, is thought to be the main reason. Look at the Cerulean Warbler Range Map.

## Habitat Loss in the Wintering Range

By 2025, there will be 100 million more people in South America than there were in 2002. As human population size increases, the demands on the land and local habitats also increase. Forests are cleared and habitats for native plants and animals are lost to make room for planting crops and for raising cattle. These crops and cattle are needed to feed the increased population of people in the area.

Cerulean warblers inhabit the dense, evergreen forests that grow at middle elevations in the Andes Mountains. Their preferred habitat is tall, mature trees where they can feed on insects.

**Cerulean Warbler Range Map**

EQUATOR

KEY

Breeding range (April–Spetember)

Wintering range (October–March)

Migration route

However, this habitat is also the preferred area to grow shade-coffee crops. The tall trees provide shade for the shorter coffee plants. Shade-coffee takes longer to grow and produces less coffee than sun-grown coffee crops. Forested areas are often cleared to make room for sun-grown coffee and other more profitable crops needing direct sunlight. This reduces the size of the warbler's habitat. As shown in the graph, the rate of clearing has decreased in recent years because the forests that are left are on steep slopes. These steep slopes and high elevations are not suitable for farming. Look at the bar graph below.

**Use the graph to answer the following questions.**

1. **CCC Patterns** Describe any patterns you see in the graph.

........................................................................

........................................................................

........................................................................

........................................................................

........................................................................

2. **Predict** What do you think the data will look like for each country in the future? Why?

........................................................................

........................................................................

........................................................................

........................................................................

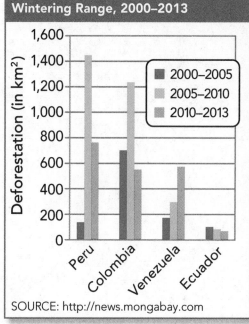

Deforestation in the Cerulean Warbler Wintering Range, 2000–2013

SOURCE: http://news.mongabay.com

3. **SEP Construct Explanations** Explain how you think changing levels of deforestation in the wintering range affects the cerulean warbler population.

........................................................................

........................................................................

4. **SEP Design Solutions** What are some strategies that you think can be used in northern South America to stabilize and protect the warbler populations?

........................................................................

........................................................................

# Take Notes

Use this space for recording notes and sketching out ideas.

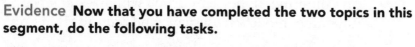
**Evidence** **Now that you have completed the two topics in this segment, do the following tasks.**

Although many people assume that mining for gold is a thing of the past in California, this is not true. Large- and small-scale mining operations still persist. Some modern miners use a technique called suction dredging to locate gold in California riverbeds. Sediment from riverbeds along with water is mechanically sucked into a machine that separates the gold from the rest of the sediment. The mixture of sediment and water is then pumped back into the river.

**Promote Student Discourse** With a partner, discuss the potential impacts of suction dredging on California ecosystems. Work together to complete a concept map to identify some of these impacts. Consider the following questions:

- What are the impacts on the abiotic and biotic factors in an ecosystem?

- How is the availability of resources in an ecosystem affected?

- How might food webs in the ecosystem be disrupted?

- How might humans be impacted by these changes?

Impacts of
Suction Dredging

# Mining Versus Wildlife

**Case Study** Suction dredging is a controversial mining method. Some people argue that it damages local ecosystems beyond repair. Miners think differently. You will now play the role of researcher to find out more about suction dredging in California. In particular, you will investigate how suction dredging impacts ecosystems and organisms in California.

Remember, when doing research online, you need to carefully evaluate the websites and information you find. The following suggestions may help you as you conduct your research:

- Use search phrases that are specific to the subject you are researching, such as *California*, *suction dredging*, *environment*.

- Beware of sites that may be biased or are trying to sell something. Ask yourself, "Why might the author of this website be taking this stance on the topic?"

- Generally, websites that end in *.gov* or *.edu* are more reliable than websites that end in *.com*.

- Take notes as you research and keep a list of the sites you find useful.

A suction dredge uses a motor, so it allows miners to quickly sort through large amounts of sediment.

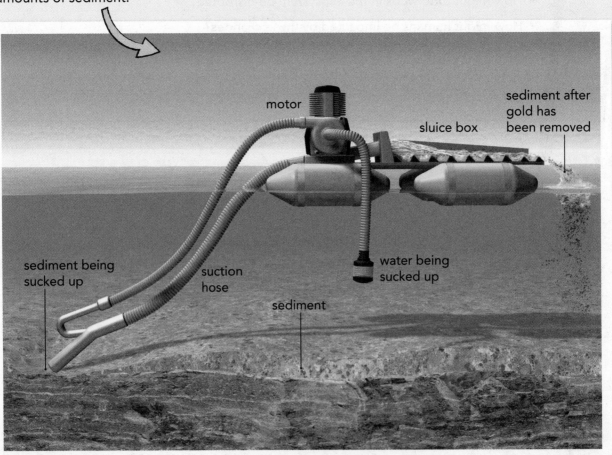

motor

sluice box

sediment after gold has been removed

sediment being sucked up

suction hose

water being sucked up

sediment

**Based on your research, answer the following questions.**

1. **SEP Construct Explanations** Is suction dredging an issue that everyone across the state in California needs to be concerned with, or do you think the concern is limited to specific areas? Explain.

.................................................................................................................

.................................................................................................................

.................................................................................................................

.................................................................................................................

.................................................................................................................

2. **CCC Cause and Effect** Which California species are affected by suction dredging? What impact does this mining method have on the availability of resources and population sizes?

.................................................................................................................

.................................................................................................................

.................................................................................................................

.................................................................................................................

.................................................................................................................

.................................................................................................................

3. **SEP Engage in Argument** What arguments have the miners made to convince people that they should be allowed to continue mining using this method? Do you think their arguments are valid? Why or why not?

.................................................................................................................

.................................................................................................................

.................................................................................................................

.................................................................................................................

.................................................................................................................

4. **Connect to Society** What is the current law in California regarding suction dredging? Would you recommend that other states pass similar laws? Why or why not?

.................................................................................................................

.................................................................................................................

.................................................................................................................

.................................................................................................................

# Safety Symbols

These symbols warn of possible dangers in the laboratory and remind you to work carefully.

**Safety Goggles** Wear safety goggles to protect your eyes in any activity involving chemicals, flames or heating, or glassware.

**Lab Apron** Wear a laboratory apron to protect your skin and clothing from damage.

**Breakage** Handle breakable materials, such as glassware, with care. Do not touch broken glassware.

**Heat-Resistant Gloves** Use an oven mitt or other hand protection when handling hot materials, such as hot plates or hot glassware.

**Plastic Gloves** Wear disposable plastic gloves when working with harmful chemicals and organisms. Keep your hands away from your face, and dispose of the gloves according to your teacher's instructions.

**Heating** Use a clamp or tongs to pick up hot glassware. Do not touch hot objects with your bare hands.

**Flames** Before you work with flames, tie back loose hair and clothing. Follow your teacher's instructions about lighting and extinguishing flames.

**No Flames** When using flammable materials, make sure there are no flames, sparks, or other exposed heat sources present.

**Corrosive Chemical** Avoid getting acid or other corrosive chemicals on your skin or clothing or in your eyes. Do not inhale the vapors. Wash your hands after the activity.

**Poison** Do not let any poisonous chemical come into contact with your skin, and do not inhale its vapors. Wash your hands when you are finished with the activity.

**Fumes** Work in a well-ventilated area when harmful vapors may be involved. Avoid inhaling vapors directly. Test an odor only when directed to do so by your teacher, and use a wafting motion to direct the vapor toward your nose.

**Sharp Object** Scissors, scalpels, knives, needles, pins, and tacks can cut your skin. Always direct a sharp edge or point away from yourself and others.

**Animal Safety** Treat live or preserved animals or animal parts with care to avoid harming the animals or yourself. Wash your hands when you are finished with the activity.

**Plant Safety** Handle plants only as directed by your teacher. If you are allergic to certain plants, tell your teacher; do not do an activity involving those plants. Avoid touching harmful plants such as poison ivy. Wash your hands when you are finished with the activity.

**Electric Shock** To avoid electric shock, never use electrical equipment around water, when the equipment is wet, or when your hands are wet. Be sure cords are untangled and cannot trip anyone. Unplug equipment not in use.

**Physical Safety** When an experiment involves physical activity, avoid injuring yourself or others. Alert your teacher if there is any reason you should not participate.

**Disposal** Dispose of chemicals and other laboratory materials safely. Follow the instructions from your teacher.

**Hand Washing** Wash your hands thoroughly when finished with an activity. Use soap and warm water. Rinse well.

**General Safety Awareness** When this symbol appears, follow the instructions provided. When you are asked to develop your own procedure in a lab, have your teacher approve your plan.

Use this space for recording notes and sketching out ideas.

# GLOSSARY

## A

**abiotic factor** A nonliving part of an organism's habitat.

**alluvial fan** A wide, sloping deposit of sediment formed where a stream leaves a mountain range.

**autotroph** An organism that is able to capture energy from sunlight or chemicals and use it to produce its own food.

## B

**biodiversity** The number and variety of different species in an area.

**biotic factor** A living or once living part of an organism's habitat.

**boiling point** The temperature at which a liquid boils.

## C

**cellular respiration** The process in which oxygen and glucose undergo a complex series of chemical reactions inside cells, releasing energy.

**chemical change** A change in which one or more substances combine or break apart to form new substances.

**chemical property** A characteristic of a substance that describes its ability to change into different substances.

**chemical weathering** The process that breaks down rock through chemical changes.

**chlorophyll** A green photosynthetic pigment found in the chloroplasts of plants, algae, and some bacteria.

**closed system** A system in which no matter is allowed to enter or leave.

**commensalism** A type of symbiosis between two species in which one species benefits and the other species is neither helped nor harmed.

**community** All the different populations that live together in a certain area.

**competition** The struggle between organisms to survive as they attempt to use the same limited resources in the same place at the same time.

**compression** Stress that squeezes rock until it folds or breaks.

**condensation** The change in state from a gas to a liquid.

**conservation** The practice of using less of a resource so that it can last longer.

**consumer** An organism that obtains energy by feeding on other organisms.

**continental glacier** A glacier that covers much of a continent or large island.

**convergent boundary** A plate boundary where two plates move toward each other.

**crust** The layer of rock that forms Earth's outer surface.

**crystal** A solid in which the atoms are arranged in a pattern that repeats again and again.

**crystallization** The process by which atoms are arranged to form a material with a crystal structure.

**crystallize** To form a crystal structure.

## D

**decomposer** An organism that gets energy by breaking down biotic wastes and dead organisms and returns raw materials to the soil and water.

**deflation** The process by which wind removes surface materials.

**delta** A landform made of sediment that is deposited where a river flows into an ocean or lake.

**density** The measurement of how much mass of a substance is contained in a given volume.

**deposition** Process in which sediment is laid down in new locations.

**desalination** A process that removes salt from sea water to make fresh water.

**divergent boundary** A plate boundary where two plates move away from each other.

**dormant** Term used to describe a volcano that is not currently acrtive but able to become active in the future.

**drought** A long period of low precipitation.

## E

**earthquake** The shaking that results from the movement of rock beneath Earth's surface.

**ecological restoration** The practice of helping a degraded or destroyed ecosystem recover from damage.

**ecology** The study of how organisms interact with each other and their environment.

**ecosystem** The community of organisms that live in a particular area, along with their nonliving environment.

**ecosystem services** The benefits that humans derive from ecosystems.

**element** A pure substance that cannot be broken down into other substances by chemical or physical means.

**energy pyramid** A diagram that shows the amount of energy that moves from one feeding level to another in a food web.

**erosion** The process by which water, ice, wind, or gravity moves weathered particles of rock and soil.

**evaporation** The process by which molecules at the surface of a liquid absorb enough energy to change to a gas.

**extinct volcano** Term used to describe a volcano that is no longer active and unlikely to erupt again

**extinction** The disappearance of all members of a species from Earth.

## F

**fault** A break in Earth's crust along which rocks move.

**fermentation** The process by which cells release energy by breaking down food molecules without using oxygen.

**flood** An overflowing of water in a normally dry area.

**flood plain** The flat, wide area of land along a river.

**food chain** A series of events in an ecosystem in which organisms transfer energy by eating and by being eaten.

**food web** The pattern of overlapping feeding relationships or food chains among the various organisms in an ecosystem.

**fossil fuel** Energy-rich substance formed from the remains of organisms.

**freezing point** The temperature at which a liquid freezes.

## G

**gas** A state of matter with no definite shape or volume.

**glacier** Any large mass of ice that moves slowly over land.

**groundwater** Water that fills the cracks and spaces in underground soil and rock layers.

## H

**habitat** An environment that provides the things a specific organism needs to live, grow, and reproduce.

**heterotroph** An organism that cannot make its own food and gets food by consuming other living things.

**hot spot** An area where magma from deep within the mantle melts through the crust above it.

**humus** Dark-colored organic material in soil.

**hurricane** A tropical storm that has winds of about 119 kilometers per hour or higher.

## I

**ice age** Time in Earth's history during which glaciers covered large parts of the surface.

**igneous rock** A type of rock that forms from the cooling of molten rock at or below the surface.

**inner core** A dense sphere of solid iron and nickel at the center of Earth.

**invasive species** Species that are not native to a habitat and can out-compete native species in an ecosystem.

# GLOSSARY

## K

**keystone species** A species that influences the survival of many other species in an ecosystem.

## L

**lava** Liquid magma that reaches the surface.

**limiting factor** An environmental factor that causes a population to decrease in size.

**liquid** A state of matter that has no definite shape but has a definite volume.

**loess** A wind-formed deposit made of fine particles of clay and silt.

**longshore drift** The movement of water and sediment down a beach caused by waves coming in to shore at an angle.

## M

**magma** A molten mixture of rock-forming substances, gases, and water from the mantle.

**magnitude** The measurement of an earthquake's strength based on seismic waves and movement along faults.

**mantle** The layer of hot, solid material between Earth's crust and core.

**mass** A measure of how much matter is in an object.

**mass movement** Any one of several processes by which gravity moves sediment downhill.

**matter** Anything that has mass and takes up space.

**mechanical weathering** The type of weathering in which rock is physically broken into smaller pieces.

**melting point** The temperature at which a substance changes from a solid to a liquid; the same as the freezing point, or temperature at which a liquid changes to a solid.

**metamorphic rock** A type of rock that forms from an existing rock that is changed by heat, pressure, or chemical reactions.

**mid-ocean ridge** An undersea mountain chain where new ocean floor is produced; a divergent plate boundary under the ocean.

**mineral** A naturally occurring solid that can form by inorganic processes and that has a crystal structure and a definite chemical composition.

**mutualism** A type of symbiosis in which both species benefit from living together.

## N

**natural resource** Anything naturally occuring in the environment that humans use.

**neutron** A small particle in the nucleus of the atom, with no electrical charge.

**nonrenewable resource** A natural resource that is not replaced in a useful time frame.

**nuclear fission** The splitting of an atom's nuclues into two nuclei, which releases a great deal of energy.

## O

**ocean trench** An undersea valley that represents one of the deepest parts of the ocean.

**open system** A system in which matter can enter from or escape to the surroundings.

**ore** A mineral deposit large enough and valuable enough for it to be extracted from the ground.

**organism** A living thing.

**outer core** A layer of molten iron and nickel that surrounds the inner core of Earth.

## P

**parasitism** A type of symbiosis in which one organism lives with, on, or in a host and harms it.

**petroleum** Liquid fossil fuel; oil.

**photosynthesis** The process by which plants and other autotrophs capture and use light energy to make food from carbon dioxide and water.

**physical change** A change that alters the form or appearance of a material but does not make the material into another substance.

**physical property** A characteristic of a pure substance that can be observed without changing it into another substance.

**pioneer species** The first species to populate an area during succession.

**plucking** The process by which a glacier picks up rocks as it flows over the land.

**polymer** A long chain of molecules made up of repeating units.

**population** All the members of one species living in the same area.

**precipitation** Any form of water that falls from clouds and reaches Earth's surface as rain, snow, sleet, or hail.

**predation** An interaction in which one organism kills another for food or nutrients.

**producer** An organism that can make its own food.

**product** A substance formed as a result of a chemical reaction.

─────────── **R** ───────────

**reactant** A substance that enters into a chemical reaction.

**rock cycle** A series of processes on the surface and inside Earth that slowly changes rocks from one kind to another.

**runoff** Water that flows over the ground surface rather than soaking into the ground.

─────────── **S** ───────────

**sand dune** A deposit of wind-blown sand.

**sea-floor spreading** The process by which molten material adds new oceanic crust to the ocean floor.

**sediment** Small, solid pieces of material that come from rocks or the remains of organisms; earth materials deposited by erosion.

**sedimentary rock** A type of rock that forms when particles from other rocks or the remains of plants and animals are pressed and cemented together.

**seismic wave** Vibrations that travel through Earth carrying the energy released during an earthquake.

**shearing** Stress that pushes masses of rock in opposite directions, in a sideways movement.

**soil** The loose, weathered material on Earth's surface in which plants can grow.

**solid** A state of matter that has a definite shape and a definite volume.

**storm** A violent disturbance in the atmosphere.

**storm surge** A "dome" of water that sweeps across the coast where a hurricane lands.

**stream** A channel through which water is continually flowing downhill.

**stress** A force that acts on rock to change its shape or volume.

**subduction** The process by which oceanic crust sinks beneath a deep-ocean trench and back into the mantle at a convergent plate boundary.

**sublimation** The change in state from a solid directly to a gas without passing through the liquid state.

**substance** A single kind of matter that is pure and has a specific set of properties.

**succession** The series of predictable changes that occur in a community over time.

**sustainability** The ability of an ecosystem to maintain bioviersity and production indefinitely.

**symbiosis** Any relationship in which two species live closely together and that benefits at least one of the species.

**synthetic** Created or manufactured by humans; not found occuring in nature

─────────── **T** ───────────

**temperature** How hot or cold something is; a measure of the average energy of motion of the particles of a substance; the measure of the average kinetic energy of the particles of a substance.

**tension** Stress that stretches rock so that it becomes thinner in the middle.

**thermal energy** The total kinetic and potential energy of all the particles of an object.

# GLOSSARY

**thunderstorm**  A small storm often accompanied by heavy precipitation and frequent thunder and lightning.

**till**  The sediments deposited directly by a glacier.

**tornado**  A rapidly whirling, funnel-shaped cloud that reaches down to touch Earth's surface.

**transform boundary**  A plate boundary where two plates move past each other in opposite directions.

**tributary**  A stream or river that flows into a larger river.

**tsunami**  A giant wave usually caused by an earthquake beneath the ocean floor.

## U

**uniformitarianism**  The geologic principle that the same geologic processes that operate today operated in the past to change Earth's surface.

## V

**valley glacier**  A long, narrow glacier that forms when snow and ice build up in a mountain valley.

**vaporization**  The change of state from a liquid to a gas.

**volcano**  A weak spot in the crust where magma has come to the surface.

**volume**  The amount of space that matter occupies.

## W

**weight**  A measure of the force of gravity acting on an object.

# CREDITS

## Photography

Photo locators denoted as follows: Top (T), Center (C), Bottom (B), Left (L), Right (R), Background (Bkgd)

### Covers

Front: James Mattil/Zoonar GmbH/Alamy Stock Photo; Stocktrek Images, Inc./Alamy Stock Photo; Casey Kiernan/Moment/Getty Images; Meganopierson/Shutterstock; Back: Marinello/DigitalVision Vectors/Getty Images

### Instructional Segment 3

iv: Nick Lundgren/Shutterstock; vi: Jeff J Daly/Alamy Stock Photo; vii: Brian J. Skerry/National Geographic/Getty Images; viii: Bkgrd: Brian J. Skerry/National Geographic/Getty Images; viiiT: Fabriziobalconi/Fotolia; ixB: Dale Kolke/ZUMA Press/Newscom; 000: Andrew J. Russell/Everett Collection Historical/Alamy Stock Photo; 001: Andrew J. Russell/Everett Collection Historical/Alamy Stock Photo; 002: TopFoto/The Image Works; 003: Marcel Clemens/Shutterstock; 004BL: Don Bendickson/AGE Fotostock; 004BR: History Images/Alamy Stock Photo; 005: Andrew J. Russell/Everett Collection Historical/Alamy Stock Photo; 008: Jeff J Daly/Alamy Stock Photo; 010: Chon Kit Leong/Alamy Stock Photo; 012: Aleksandr Pobedimskiy/Shutterstock; 014: Louisiana Governors Office/Alamy Stock Photo; 016: National Geographic Creative/Alamy Stock Photo; 019: Everett Historical/Shutterstock; 022: Henryk Sadura/Shutterstock; 024: WaterFrame/Alamy Stock Photo; 025T: Shu-Hung Liu/Shutterstock; 025B: Siim Sepp/Alamy Stock Photo; 026: SuperStock/Alamy Stock Photo; 028: The Natural History Museum/Alamy Stock Photo; 032: David McNew/Newsmakers/Hulton Archive/Getty Images; 035: Bennyartist/Shutterstock; 037: Justin Sullivan/Getty Images; 040: Haizhen Du/Shutterstock; 041T: iStock/Getty Images; 041B: Anton Starikov/Alamy Stock Photo; 044: Brian J. Skerry/National Geographic/Getty Images; 046: Helen H. Richardson/The Denver Post/Getty Images; 048: Hartrey Media/Shutterstock; 050: David Litman/Shutterstock; 053: Martin Harvey/Alamy Stock Photo; 054: Awie Badenhorst/Alamy Stock Photo; 056: Design Pics/Getty Images; 061Bkgrd: Moelyn Photos/Getty Images; 061TL: Audrey Snider-Bell/Shutterstock; 061TC: Davies and Starr/Getty Images; 061TR: Jim Cumming/Getty Images; 061ML: IrinaK/Shutterstock; 061MR: Anthony Mercieca/Science Source; 061BL: Ashley Cooper/Alamy Stock Photo; 061BC: Ken Kistler/Shutterstock; 061BR: National Geographic Creative/Alamy Stock Photo; 063: Hal Beral/VWPics/AGE Fotostock; 065Bkgrd: Christopher Berkey/EPA/Alamy Stock Photo; 065TR: Christoph Gertler/Bangor University; 065MR: Stillfx/Shutterstock; 066: Somkiet Poomsiripaiboon/Shutterstock; 068: Paul Lemke/Fotolia; 070Bkgrd: Jovannig/Fotolia; 070BL: Cvalle/Shutterstock; 070BR: Aleksander Bolbot/Getty Images; 071BL: Steven Widoff/Alamy Stock Photo; 071BC: Danny Frank/Shutterstock; 071BR: Yeko Photo Studio/Shutterstock; 075T: Olha Insight/Shutterstock; 075MR: Kuttelvaserova Stuchelova/Shutterstock; 076A: Sarama/Shutterstock; 076B: David Bokuchava/Shutterstock; 076C: Apiguide/Shutterstock; 076D: Gnek/Shutterstock; 076E: Luis Castaneda Inc/Getty Images; 076F: Terry Whittaker/Alamy Stock Photo; 076G: Deposit Photos/Glow Images; 076H: Bee-Eater/Shutterstock; 076I: Miroslav Chaloupka/CTK Photo/Alamy Stock Photo; 076J: FLPA/Alamy Stock Photo; 076K: Biosphoto/Alamy Stock Photo; 076L: Biosphoto/Alamy Stock Photo; 078: Mlorenz/Shutterstock; 079L: Wildlife GmbH/Alamy Stock Photo; 079R: Loop Images Ltd/Alamy Stock Photo.

# Take Notes

Use this space for recording notes and sketching out ideas.

# Take Notes

Use this space for recording notes and sketching out ideas.

Use this space for recording notes and sketching out ideas.

# Take Notes

Use this space for recording notes and sketching out ideas.

# Take Notes

Use this space for recording notes and sketching out ideas.

# Take Notes

# Take Notes

Use this space for recording notes and sketching out ideas.

# Take Notes

Use this space for recording notes and sketching out ideas.

# Take Notes

Use this space for recording notes and sketching out ideas.

Use this space for recording notes and sketching out ideas.

# Take Notes

Use this space for recording notes and sketching out ideas.